MUR

MURUGA

MURUGA

THE LORD OF WAR,
THE GOD OF WISDOM

ANAND BALASUBRAMANIAN

RUPA

Published by
Rupa Publications India Pvt. Ltd 2021
7/16, Ansari Road, Daryaganj
New Delhi 110002

Sales centres:
Allahabad Bengaluru Chennai
Hyderabad Jaipur Kathmandu
Kolkata Mumbai

ISBN: 978-81-291-4495-9

First impression 2021

10 9 8 7 6 5 4 3 2 1

The moral right of the author has been asserted.

Printed at Thomson Press India Ltd, Faridabad

Contents

Daksha Parva

Daksha	3
Sukhra	6
Surasai	8

Sura Parva

Kashyapa	13
Parvati	17
Mahadeva	20
Indra	22
Jayanta	24
Sura	26
Yuddha	28
Mahavishnu	33
Veeramahendrapuri	36
Shraap	41
Hope	44
Confrontation	46
Ajamukhi	51

Indra Parva

Indrani	57
Wrath	60
Indra	63
Kamadeva	64
Rati	67

Nandi   69
Ananga   72
Parvati   74
Mainavati   77
Nuptial   80
Durvasa   84
Indra   86

Kumarasambhava

Kumarasambhava   91
Ganesha   95
Kritikas   99
Cheyyon   101
Meru   104
Narada!   107
Jnanaphala   109
Idumba   111
Avvai   114
Clan   118
Reunion   121
Brahma   123
Swaminatha   126
Devayani   129
Shaktivel   132

Yuddha Parva

Vatapi   137
Mayapuri   141
Krauncha   146
Plan   151

Chendur   154
Asurendran   157
Veerabahu   161
Negotiations   165
Vajrabahu   169
Jayanta   172
Samudra   174
Mourning   177
Prathama   181
Dwitiya   186
Tritiya   197
Chaturthi   206
Panchami   214
Kandashasti   225

Shanta Parva

Aftermath   241
Sunk   245
Celebrations   246
Clampdown   249
Dawn   251

Prema Parva

Nambiraja   259
Valli   260
Hunter   262
Old Man   266
Marriage   271
Harmony   275

Daksha Parva

Daksha

'Daksha!' shrieked Veerabhadra's shrill voice. It sent trembling waves of fear down the spine of every single Deva, rishi, Danava, Gandharva and Naga. It did not even spare Brahma or Vishnu. Veerabhadra was death personified, a form of the single most destructive force that is supposed to come only at the end of times to kill the invincible. Daksha ran as fast as he could, clawing his way through the numerous guests who had come to attend his yagna.

Veerabhadra walked through the guests like a red-hot knife slicing butter, taking lives as a storm would collect flowers if it were to pass through a garden. Daksha realized that he had pushed things too far. He knew that his time was up. There was no escape. Yet, fear propelled him forward, fast.

Daksha could feel hot breath on his neck. He wanted to turn around, to beg for mercy. He wanted to stay alive. It was no longer a matter of choice for him: he had done irreparable damage to Mahadeva and now he had to pay the price. After all, he had let his daughter die, preferring to satiate his ego over his love for his daughter or respect for the supreme lord. As his golden shawl caught fire, he realized that the end was near. In a couple of seconds, everything would be over, but these last seconds stretched on. His entire life played out in front of his eyes like a film: he saw his mistakes, especially those which led to the dreadful fate that awaited him. Running was futile, but he still ran impulsively. He had hoped that Vishnu could stop his tormentor, and to be fair, being the preserver, Vishnu did throw his Sudarshan Chakra at Veerabhadra.

The fearless and peerless warrior that Veerabhadra was, he merely opened his mouth and swallowed the Chakra whole and continued after his target, Daksha. However, that did not deter Vishnu, for he was duty bound. Using his full might, he imprisoned

Veerabhadra by creating a cage through his power and control over Maya. Since Veerabhadra was one with Mahadeva, his current predicament became instantly known to Mahadeva, who threw down another lock of hair, like he had done to create Veerabhadra, and from it sprang Bhadrakali. She was an aspect of Kali, the most fearsome, powerful and unstoppable form of Shakti. She was said to be the kinder aspect and, without the presence of Sati on earth, the source of her perineal energy was limited.

Bhadrakali immediately appeared at Daksha's yagna. She opened her third eye and a bolt of energy radiated from it in the form of a Trisula, which went straight towards the cage that had imprisoned Veerabhadra and freed him. Vishnu, having done all he could and to the best of his abilities, only because he was obligated to, decided to leave Daksha to his fate.

Daksha was fleeing, but Bhadrakali appeared before him, forcing him to change direction. No matter where he turned, she appeared in her fearsome form with eight hands, each wielding a different instrument of death, scaring him even more. There was only one direction left for him, which took him to Veerabhadra.

As he continued fleeing, Daksha could smell his hair burning. His head was forcefully turned backwards while his feet ran forward and he was lifted bodily in the air. Tears rolled from his eyes as other bodily fluids leaked out of his orifices. Everything was involuntary: he had no control over his body. He saw Veerabhadra breathing fire, his brain registered the image but his body failed to react in a logical manner. Like severing the head of a chicken, Veerabhadra took Daksha's head off his body. His headless body continued to move, propelled by the momentum it had gained: it ran ahead a couple of yards before falling. The legs kicked a few times before the body stilled on the floor.

Veerabhadra had completed the task he had been called for. He calmed down and his dishevelled appearance became normal. The moment he threw down Daksha's head, Mahadeva appeared.

Upon seeing Mahadeva, Veerabhadra went to him. The Chakra fell and went to Vishnu as Veerabhadra's body disappeared, merging with the supreme lord. Bhadrakali followed suit.

Mahadeva looked around and saw total carnage. The stench of blood, singed flesh and burnt hair filled the air. He approached the yagnashala: in the flames, he saw what was left of his wife, Dakshayani's body. He could not hold himself back. He was no longer Mahadeva; he now was Rudra, the husband who had lost his wife whom he loved to no end.

Rudra let out a cry, slung the charred body over his shoulders and started dancing. It was not his graceful Anandatandavam, but the dreaded Rudratandavam. It was a dance that began to shake the very foundation of the multiverse. It was the final dance, meant for the end of time and space, except that it was not the end of time yet. Devas, Gandharvas and rishis, or whatever was left of them, ran to Vishnu. They begged him to put an end to this. Vishnu took his Sudarshan Chakra and cast it at Dakshayani's corpse. It cut her into one thousand and eight pieces which landed in different parts of the universe.

With the weight off his shoulders, Shiva fell to his knees and started crying like a mere mortal. Vishnu, his dearest friend and peacemaker unparalleled, hugged and consoled him. He reminded Shiva of who he really was and that he knew all along this was how things were to be. Shiva rose and went back to Kailash. There, he sat down, and by the time the final tear rolled down his cheek, he was already in deep meditation. He was lost to the world and the world was lost to him.

Nandi, seeing all this, cursed that everyone would pay dearly for this. He spared none, saying that all of them would suffer untold misfortune and torture for a millennium for the way events had turned out. He also went back and took his position as the guard of Kailash.

Brahma, Daksha's father, could not bear to see his beloved

son die. His guilt was eating him because he knew that he could have interfered and stopped his son. Vishnu and Brahma together restored whoever and whatever they could to normal order. The Devas who were still alive, by virtue of drinking Amrut, grew back their limbs. The dead ones were gone for good. After all, no amount of Amrut can save you from an aspect of Sadasiva, be it Veerabhadra or Mahakaal or Shiva.

Daksha's head was lost. Brahma found a goat meant for sacrifice, severed its head and connected it to Daksha's body, its legs still kicking, bringing both back to life. The guests who survived were relieved that they had managed to avert a total disaster. Little did they know that the worst was yet to come in the form of Nandi's curse. Vishnu, Brahma and a few others, who could see and knew, were quiet as it was not for them to interfere in this. They played their part through their silence till it was too late to change anything. With Daksha's head gone, one of the strongest reagents and supporters of the Devas was no more. With the loss of his power, the balance of the universe tilted to one side, the side of the sworn enemies of the Devas, the Asuras.

Sukhra

Sukhra was reeling. He and his disciples had constantly been humiliated, defeated and cheated of their rights by the Devas, especially by Indra, his guru Brihaspati and the ever-scheming Vishnu. They had been cheated during the churning of the ocean, when the Devas took all the Amrut.

Sukhra was a fair person. He assessed the Asuras as cocky, arrogant and full of pride, unlike their stepbrothers the Devas, which led them to underestimate their adversary. This character trait always led to their downfall. However, he knew that his time had come with the unfolding of the events at Daksha's yagna.

He summoned his beloved disciple Surasai, who was also known as Maya. It was not a mere nickname. It was a title she had earned by virtue of excelling in illusionary art under his tutelage. She was capable of creating a whole new planet, albeit virtual. She could trick anyone, or almost anyone. Surasai was someone who would lay down her life without questioning if her guru ordered it. She stood before him with her head bent, awaiting his instructions.

Sukhra said, 'Go to the father of the Devas, Sage Kashyapa, and have as many children as possible with him. They should be so powerful that they get the full potential of penance from the great sage and the full benefit of your powers and control over Maya. Take the form of different powerful creatures when you make love with him and beget children imbued with the power of your Maya, his penance and the animal's characteristics. These children will revive the Asuras; they will take us back to the top.

'Under my tutelage, with your Maya and the sage's power, we will bring back our glory of the days when the Asura flag flew high across the universe. Remember the mantras I taught you to give life to objects. Don't waste a single drop of sweat that comes out of him: they too contain an essence of his power. Your progeny will rule the multiverse. They will make the worlds tremble at the mere mention of their names. They will make the vile Devas our slaves. All the credit, my dear child, will come to you. They will place all the worlds at your feet and avenge the ignominy and dishonour that the Asuras had to suffer at the hands of the Devas. Seek your parents' permission and get their approval before you leave.'

'I will do as you order, esteemed teacher. I will place the world and the children at your feet, O peerless one! You, who has always looked out for the best interest of the Asuras, will be obeyed without question. My parents will not utter a single word that goes against your will. Still, I will ask for their permission, get their approval and then proceed to honour your word,' said

Surasai. She closed her eyes and thought of her parents. Through her powers, she made their ethereal form appear before them. The guru was pleased with the prowess of her powers, her intelligence in using them and at her obedience.

'Father! Mother! Our guru has ordered me to marry Kashyapa and beget children to revive the Asuras and bring back the days of our glory. He has ordered me to take your blessings before I leave,' said Surasai. Her father, the Asura king Atisuran, and his wife, without hesitation, in one voice, said, 'Dear child, you will always have our blessings. Our esteemed guru's words are final. You didn't have to seek our permission or even inform us. Our guru has our best interest in his mind. Do as he says, and we will be proud of you!'

Surasai took the blessings of all three and left.

Surasai

Surasai went to the forest where Sage Kashyapa was in deep penance. With one stroke of her finger, she created the most beautiful garden ever seen. At the centre of it, she created a palace filled with life-like sculptures of humans, oozing love, sex and romance. The fragrant flowers in the garden attracted all the animals in the forest and she created abundant food for them. She then turned herself into the most beautiful and irresistible woman to have ever existed.

She started playing the veena and singing in a mellifluous voice. The birds joined her in song. With the whole forest now heaving with smell, sight, sound and taste, it was only a matter of time before Sage Kashyapa turned his attention towards the source. He, like all creatures in the garden, was smitten. As he went closer to the palace, he became more and more enamoured with the experience. At the centre of the palace, he saw Maya. He could not contain himself and rushed to her. He asked her who she was and how she had created the place.

Maya replied coyly that she had no idea. Like him, she too had been attracted by the beauty of the place. The rishi, forgetting himself, asked her to be his wife. She said that she was an ordinary young girl, while he was a very old and revered rishi. She rejected his advances and disappeared into the garden, leaving Kashyapa desolate. He searched for her throughout the garden for days, and his hunger for her plunged him further into despair. She occupied his entire mind, the same mind which had been originally filled with thoughts of Paramashiva.

Soon, Maya reappeared in the garden, sitting by the lake and playing with a deer. Like water rushes into a deep trench, happiness, joy and lust filled Kashyapa's empty heart and soul the very moment he saw her. He rushed to her side and sat by her feet, surrendering himself to her unconditionally. She smiled, realizing that she had him under her control and would get anything she wants.

Maya looked at Kashyapa with eyes full of wonder, as if she was seeing him for the very first time.

'What do you want, O great sage?' she asked him.

Kashyapa was crestfallen. She didn't remember his plea. His hope, that she had come back to become his, was dashed to the ground. Tears fell from his eyes.

'Don't you remember? Why are you doing this to me? Why did you come to this earth? Why did you come to this forest? Why did you come before my eyes? Why did you look at me? Why did you smile at me? Why did you disappear? Why did you come back again instead of letting me die? Why are you killing me repeatedly by denying me your beauty?' cried the sage.

'O great sage! I am merely a mortal who, like everyone else, has little choice in where life takes me. I do what I must do. I will accede to your request, but I...'

He did not let her finish her sentence. He jumped in joy: by a word, accede, she had given him life. He was lifted to the highest of heavens hearing the word. Nothing else mattered to him at that instant. He moved towards her.

'Stop, O seer! I have some conditions,' Maya said.

'I accept,' Kashyapa replied, rushing closer.

'Hear me out, O great one!' Maya disappeared like camphor and reappeared across the lake. 'I am a young girl and you are a very old sage. I do not find you attractive in this form. And, if someone were to see me with you, I would lose my honour. I will be yours if you, using your great powers, take the form I ask you to when we make love. Also, if, even for a second, you were to think of anything else but me, I will leave you for sure and take everything I gave you with me. These are my conditions.'

'I accept,' the sage repeated as he ran towards Maya.

'Let us go inside the palace, O noble one!' Maya guided him into the palace.

Sura Parva

Kashyapa

Maya led Kashyapa into the palace. The beautiful palace paled in comparison to his companion. She led him deeper and deeper inside the palace as his mind sank deeper and deeper into her eyes. She could see that she had him where she wanted.

'O great sage! I am not attracted to you. You look haggard and old. I am a beautiful young girl. I want my son to be handsome, young and powerful. If you want me now, you need to change your form and become the most powerful, virile and handsome young man possible,' said Surasai to the enamoured sage.

'Your word is my life,' said Kashyapa as he transformed mid-sentence into a male form that was both awe-inspiring and fear-inducing at the same time. Without letting her utter another word, he pounced on her and she acquiesced. After she exhausted him, she begot a son whose face shone like a bright red lotus in full bloom shining in the light of the full moon. The son's body belied the fact that he was a newborn: he was muscular and strong, and his first cry sent a terrifying shockwave across the forest. All the animals ran helter-skelter in fear and the birds that could not take off quickly enough dropped down dead. Maya christened the boy Surapadma.

Surasai also chanted the mantra her guru had taught her, and it turned all the sweat accumulated from the sage's body in the course of their lovemaking into Asuras, one Asura for every drop.

Kashyapa, however, was unaware of these happenings, as he was still besotted by Maya's beauty. The Asuras she created from his sweat were not visible to the sage, not that he took his eyes off her to see his surroundings. He did not even take the time to see his son. For him, all he could ever see, was Surasai.

Kashyapa went back to Maya as soon as he regained his senses. He wanted her again, and this time she took the form of a giant powerful lioness. There was no room for fear in the heart of the sage, for it was filled with lust. He transformed himself into the most fearsome lion that ever existed and they made love again. This time, Surasai birthed another son, who was even more fearsome. He had a lion's head and a humongous human body, and when he let out a cry, the forest trembled in fear. Maya called him Simhamukha. Just like last time, she turned every single drop of the sage's sweat into Asuras.

The sage was physically too exhausted and mentally too involved with Surasai to notice what was going on around him. This time, when he regained his energy, she still looked as beautiful as ever. The night had not even passed, and he felt like he had lived two full lifetimes with her. He wanted her even more now, so he approached her again. She quickly turned herself into an elephant of mammoth proportions. The sage transformed himself into an even bigger elephant and made love to her. He begot another son, whom she named Taraka, with the head of a fully-grown mammoth and a monstrous human body. He also had millions of brothers, born from the sweat of the sage.

The exhausted Kashyapa could not keep up with her due to his age. His lust however did not let him rest. As he approached her again, she turned into a goat, forcing him to turn into a ram. However, this time, she was the more powerful one. They made love and begot a girl child with the head of a goat. All this child could inherit from the sage was his overwhelming lust, as the other three had already got his strength and power. Ajamukhi or the goat-faced one, as she was called by Surasai, also had a million brothers.

Seeing that the sage was getting exhausted, Surasai wanted to make the most of the situation. Whenever the sage got up, she put on various animal forms, increasingly smaller in size, to help the sage keep up with her. Each time, a son or a daughter was born, thousands of Asuras accompanied it.

As the sun rose, the sage was completely drained and exhausted.

His lust did not subside but his energy did. Seeing that he was no longer useful, Surasai introduced her first four children to him. They sought his blessings and the sage blessed them that they will live for over a hundred and eight yugas. The power of his penance meant that his words would never be futile. Having got everything she wanted from Kashyapa, Surasai sought to take the children away from his shadow so that her true mission could be fulfilled.

Surapadma, being the eldest, asked, 'O Father! Kindly tell us how to live our life.' The sage answered, 'Pray to Lord Shiva.' The moment he uttered the name of Shiva, the palace, the garden, all the Maya created by Surasai, disappeared. Kashyapa's mind was now completely immersed in Shiva and he slipped into a deep trance and without speaking another word, sat down in the same place and started his penance.

Seizing the opportunity, Surasai told her children, 'Do not to disturb your father, my children.' She took them away from him and said, 'Children, do as your father ordered. Perform severe penance to Shiva, please him and get the boon that you will rule the universe for as long as you live. Once you have got that boon, come and meet me. I will be at the ashrama of our family guru, Sukhracharya.'

'O Mother, the purpose of our life is to obey the order of the ones who begot us. We will do as you ordered,' said the three children in chorus and they ventured south. Ajamukhi accompanied Surasai to Sukhracharya's ashram.

Sura and his brothers walked on with the rest of the Asuras, leaving his sister Ajamukhi and his mother Surasai behind. The earth trembled with their march and the sound their footsteps shook the heavens. Indra, being his usual paranoid self, ran to find out what had happened overnight. Narada met him on the way. Narada, the one who can travel all the worlds, told him what had happened and Indra merely scoffed.

Sukhra met Sura and his brothers on the way, blessed them

and gave them mantras that would render them free of hunger and fatigue for a long time. They thanked their guru and promised him that they would return to him once they had succeeded in getting boons from Mahadeva. They marched further south and crossed the bountiful Vindhyas. It was so beautiful that it caught the fancy of Tarakasura, the elephant-headed Asura. Krauncha, a powerful demon who had taken the form of a mountain, woke up because of the activity. Upon learning that they are Asuras, he said, 'I am Krauncha the demon. I fled south after being chased off by Indra and the Devas, O scion of Asura!' His words sent a new rush of blood through Surapadma's veins.

'Fear not!' thundered Surapadma. 'I had three brothers. Now I have four,' he said. 'You will be one of us,' said Tarakasura, who took an instant liking to Krauncha and the friendship of a lifetime was born.

'If you ever see a single Deva who is not your slave cross the Vindhyas, O Sura, it means I am dead. This I promise,' Krauncha replied. He bade them farewell and went back to be a mountain.

The Asura brothers continued further south until they reached Vadadweepam (Northern Island), where they cleared the entire island of vegetation. Then they established a huge yagnashala that covered the entire span of the island, and continued their sacrifices and penance for over tens of thousands of years, powered by the mantras taught to them by their guru.

However, as Indra had anticipated, Mahadeva was in deep of meditation. There was nothing that could wake up him. Even if it did, they would only incur his wrath for disturbing him.

Surapadma also saw this. All this effort seemed to be going in vain, so he took his giant sword and cut open his arteries. Blood spewed out of his hands and gushed into the fire. Tarakasura and Simhamukha too did the same upon seeing their brother. Simhamukha went a step ahead and cut his head off and it fell into the fire. His head grew back and he repeated the action a thousand times.

Surapadma said, 'O Mahadeva, if my penance and my sacrifices have not pleased you enough, then my blood and my life will, for without your grace, there is no point in me being alive.' Saying this, he jumped into the fire and Tarakasura did the same. Seeing this, many of the Asuras followed suit. Just as Simhamukha was about to jump into the fire, an old man walked across the yagnashala.

'Who are you children and why are you killing yourselves?' exclaimed the old man. Simhamukha paused a moment, bowed to the old man and told him their story.

Water spouted from the top of the old man's head and started flowing into the yagnakunda, dousing the fire. Surapadma, Tarakasura and all the Asuras who had died in the fire stood up and the old man transformed into Lord Shiva sitting on his mount, Nandi.

Parvati

*H*imavat, the mountain king, and his beloved wife, Mainavati, were longing for a child: they wanted the goddess Shakti herself as their child. Devotees of Lord Shiva, they prayed to him day in and day out for a child. They decided to hand over the reins of their kingdom to their trusted minister and go to Mana Sarovar, the forest nearby, and engage in deep penance to attain their aim.

On an auspicious day, when the full moon was shining bright, the couple went to collect a blue lotus as a special offering to their god. The forest lake shone so bright that they could not see what or who was ahead of them, and they believed that the supreme Lord Mahadeva had himself descended to bless them with their hearts' desire as a result of their devout service and penance. The lake gleamed with the reflection of the full moon and the stars, so beautiful that one would not be wrong to mistake the reflection for the skies itself but for the beautiful blue lotuses.

Tears rolled down their cheeks when they saw a girl child with three eyes and eight hands, seated in the middle of the biggest and brightest lotus. Sati, the physical form of the divine mother and the manifestation of the primordial energy, who self-immolated on the eve of the accursed yagna of her then father, Daksha, had been waiting to be born to eventually rejoin her husband Mahadeva. She picked Himavat and Mainavati, the pious couple devoted to her lord, to make sure that there would not be a repeat of Daksha. History, as they say, is bound to repeat itself if one fails to learn from it. The divine mother knew it too well.

As soon as the couple took the child from the lotus, her third eye and six arms disappeared, rendering her a normal child. She was christened Parvati and Himavati, meaning daughter of the hills and Himavat. Considering her environment, the pious nature of her parents and her natural inclination to devotion to her husband, Mahadeva, she grew up more interested in penance and prayer over playing and frolicking.

On her fifth birthday, she ran to her mother as Mainavati beckoned her.

'What do you want my child, it is your birthday tomorrow,' said her mother. Her father joined them and told her that she would have whatever she asked for, without question, for she was the apple of their eye.

'Dear Mother, Father, I want a yagnashala. I am going to do penance,' said Parvati. The amused parents laughed together.

'Ask for whatever you want in the world, my child. Penance and yagna are meant for older people. This is your time to live life, play and have fun. Do you want a golden deer to play with? Do you want an elephant to ride everywhere? Do you want the fairest pony? Ask anything!' said her father.

'Dear Father, I have already asked what I wish. You gave your word that I would get whatever I ask for, dear Father. All I want is a yagnashala to do penance for Mahadeva, at whose feet I seek refuge,' said Uma, as they fondly called her.

Both Himavat and Mainavati were taken aback. Their five-year-old daughter's insistence on doing penance left them disconcerted, and her resolve to renounce life and seek god himself, plunged them into confusion and despair. However, they gave in, considering that Uma had always been a wilful girl. Himavat, being a wise king and a father, knew better than to oppose her move. 'I will arrange for the yagnashala, my child. Perform your penance as you see fit. As far as reaching god himself goes, I cannot help you, my child,' he said.

'Thank you, Father. Being with the lord is the purpose of my life and existence. I will either succeed or die trying. I know it is beyond our control. Without our god's grace, it cannot happen. I will, through my austere and extreme penance, please him and get the boon from him myself. Please arrange for the yagnashala to be in Mount Meru. I want only two of my best friends, Vijaya and Jaya, with me and do not want anyone else,' replied Uma as she left to pray.

'Why did you agree to what she asked for, dear husband? Don't you know that it is next to impossible to even meet our lord, let alone marry him?' asked Mainavati.

'I know that, my dear. If she succeeds, she will get to the lotus feet of god himself. If she gives up, we get our daughter back to us to marry off to an eligible prince. If she dies in her attempt to please the lord, she will again reach his lotus feet and attain Moksha. There is no outcome where our daughter's life is ruined,' replied the king.

Himavat called his minster and asked him to make the necessary arrangements for Uma's yagna and penance. He also ordered his minister to ensure that she remained protected during the entire duration of her ordeal.

All this while, Shiva had not stirred. He had been in a deep meditative trance for centuries, the one that he had slipped into after the death of his beloved wife. The honour of waking him up belonged to Surapadma's supreme sacrifice.

Mahadeva

'What do you want, O Asura? Why are you doing such a severe penance? What is it that you seek in return for such utter devotion and high sacrifice? Speak without fear, O Son!' said the benevolent Rudra.

'Mahadeva! Vishwanatha! Neelakanta! Rudra! Eswara! Shiva! You've finally graced our yagnashala with your presence. Your benevolence is unparalleled. Your kindness is deeper than the deepest of oceans and higher than the highest of skies,' Sura praised the lord. The all-knowing, all-seeing Shiva smiled.

'You will get your heart's desire if you speak it, son of Kashyapa and Maya,' said Shiva.

'O Shiva! Kindly bless us that we will rule the universe for the entirety of our lifetime, that we will forever be undefeated. Please bless us that we will not want for anything, living our entire lives in abundance for eternity,' asked Surapadma.

Considering the magnitude of the sacrifices made by the Asura brothers and the depth of their devotion, Shiva said, 'So be it. Also, since all of your brothers gave your life as a sacrifice in the yagna, none but my power will be able to defeat you. As Simhamukha sacrificed his head a thousand times, he will have a thousand heads and he will lose his life only after all his thousand heads have been removed and have stopped growing back. As he is devoted to my Shakti, his heads will stop growing back only when beheaded by my Shakti.

'Tarakasura, having devotedly followed you, will also be invincible but for my power. All three of you shall from now on have my permission to take over the multiverse and be its guardians.

'Your father had blessed you with a life of a hundred and eight yugas. For the entire time, you will rule the multiverse and not just this universe. You will live and die as emperors of the multiverse. Be benevolent, be united and, most of all, be kind to your subjects and rule wisely, O Asura!'

'Mahadeva!' continued Sura, realizing that there was an imminent death in the far future. 'Bless us that no power except yours will have the power slay us!'

Having blessed the Asuras as such, Shiva disappeared and returned to Kailash. Just as he was about to go back into his meditative trance, four people entered his presence after seeking permission from Nandi. They were the four Kumaras: Sanaka, Sanatana, Sanandana, and Sanatkumara. The four sons born of Brahma, the highest of sages and enlightened ones, had left behind all materialistic pursuits and wandered around all the worlds with the sole purpose of teaching and spreading their knowledge. They are the eternally youthful jnani and yogi. The Kumaras had refused to partake in the process of procreation for which their father Brahma sired them and instead pursued peace and knowledge.

'What is it that you seek, noble souls?' asked Shiva.

'We have learned all the Vedas, Puranas and Upanishads. We have visited all the worlds. We have seen the past, present and future. We have performed the highest of yoga and have attained jnana. We also know the path to Moksha and are following it diligently. However, we still lack one of the most important things that all beings created under you seek, O lord! We are still searching for eternal peace. We are unable to find peace in knowledge and ignorance. We are unable to find peace in renunciation as well as in indulgence. We are unable to find peace in physical or ethereal form. We are unable to find peace in this universe or any other.

O Mahadeva, kindly teach us, kindly guide us to peace!' said the
four brothers in unison.

'Sit, my children. I will disseminate the required knowledge,
the knowledge that will not only give you the peace you seek but
also Moksha!' said benevolent Shiva.

Shiva then summoned Nandi, giving him specific instructions
that he was not to be disturbed, with an exception. Then, the
four Kumaras sat down as prescribed for disciples, as did Shiva as
prescribed for a guru.

Shiva's discourse on the highest of knowledge began within
their mindspace. Not a word was uttered, not a muscle moved.
All five of them sat motionless as the discourse continued. They
left the realm of time and space as Shiva guided them into the
supreme knowledge. Nandi, seeing this, knew that no one should
be allowed inside unless the lord himself wakes up and allows it.

Indra

*H*aving received the blessings of the most powerful, there was
nothing standing between Sura and his destiny. The brothers, along
with the entire fleet of Asuras, let out a war cry that shook the
very foundations of the universe. Indra finally realized that he had
failed to comprehend the power of Nandi's curse, made a mistake
of acknowledging Daksha's yagna and, above all, underestimated
the willpower of the new Asura. Indra ran to Vaikunta, as always.
'Paramatma will help me. There is no situation where he has failed
us, the Devas,' thought Indra.

Vishnu was in anantasayana, his divine slumber. Goddess
Lakshmi must have merged with Vishnu, leaving her physical form
and going back to reside in his heart, because she was nowhere to
be seen. That was not good news, for she was kinder to the Devas.

Indra sat at Vishnu's feet and woke him up. Vishnu opened his lotus eyes and looked at Indra. With the gentlest of smiles Idhayakamalavasa said, 'It is time for us to reap what we sowed by taking part in Daksha's yagna. Time has come for Nandi's curse to take effect. We all will have to survive whatever our fate throws at us. This time, Indra, you are on your own, as am I. This threat is something that you would have never even imagined in your wildest dreams. I have only one advice for you now, Indra. Remember, this too shall change.'

Having spoken thus, Vishnu went back into this trance, to continue looking into the future to see how events were going to unfold and see through the intricate web that karma had spun around the Devas. His smile never left his lips.

Indra was now desperate. He ran to his grandfather, the grandsire and progenitor Brahma. Brahma was in meditation as well. Indra woke up Brahma, who looked at him and said nothing. Brahma patted his head once and went back to meditate.

'This is not good! You are our progenitor. You must help us. Guide us at the very least!' cried Indra. Brahma did not respond. Indra then ran to Brihaspati. His guru would help him. He would at least be more vocal and clearer on the course of action to be taken.

'It has begun,' stated Brihaspati. 'Be prepared for the worst. Hide the women in disguise among common folk. Prepare for battle. More importantly, prepare to lose in the battle, my child. Endurance is a virtue which alone can help you now. Do not get caught: if you are caught, all hope is lost for those who depend on you. Let Jayanta take the lead in battle,' said his guru.

'You are the most knowledgeable one. You surely know a way to help,' pleaded Indra.

'It is my duty to guide you in the best way possible, my child. As your guru, I have directed you in the best manner possible,' Brihaspati concluded and Indra took his leave.

Indra meandered through the forest on his way back, strategizing for the impending defeat. He decided that the best approach was to prioritize his safety. With imminent defeat, unless he was safely far away, there would be no redemption for the Devas. He decided to task his son, the fearless Jayanta, to be the general of the Devas and face the approaching Asura army, while he took on the task of escorting the women and children to safety.

Mind made up, he summoned Jayanta, his son, his heir apparent and his best warrior.

Jayanta

*J*ayanta was the son of Indra, the king of the Devas, and Indrani, an Asuri devoted to Mahadeva.

Jayanta entered and threw himself at his father's feet, seeking his blessings. 'May you live and rule for long, my son,' said Indra proudly.

'Arrange for an elaborate ceremony,' he continued as Jayanta looked at him, puzzled. Indra then commanded, 'I will be appointing you the general of our army. There is a war coming, my son. A war unlike one we have ever seen, with an enemy who we never thought we would face; a war that could challenge the very existence of our race. You will lead the army of Devas and I will take a small division with me, along with our women and children and lead them to safety.'

'Is it that bad? Is Vritra back? If so, this time, I will strike him so hard that he will never even dream of turning towards Amaravati,' said Jayanta bravely.

'No, my son,' said Indra, smiling at the brave young warrior who stood before him. 'This is not that simple. This enemy is like a thousand Vritras put together. Victory is certain, but not for us. If you remember the stories your mother told you, we Devas had participated in a yagna conducted by Daksha. We were cursed by Nandi then; the curse has come to fruition.'

'I thought they were mere stories, Father. Besides, it has been ages. Do curses work like that? Are we so powerless as to be afraid of a mere Asura, now that we are immortal?' asked Jayanta innocently.

'We are mere specks of dusts in the larger scheme of things, my son. Our power may increase to great heights and even challenge the mightiest of beings, but nothing is forever. Sadasiva is the only one who is outside the realm of space and time. He is around us as Shiva, to be a part of us, help us and eventually destroy us when the time comes. Inside the realm, Vishnu is the most powerful and our protector until the end of times. Brahma is our progenitor. All races and life forms come from Brahma and his progeny. We may live for a long time, but like all creatures, our time too shall come, and we too are mere slaves of our karma, governed by time,' said Indra.

'I am not forsaking you, Jayanta,' Indra continued, 'even though I am assigning you the task of leading the Devas into certain defeat and captivity. Keep them together, keep their morale up and when the time comes, lead them back here and to war if required. I will meanwhile work from outside and get things ready for when the time is right. Both of us will have to act to ensure that our existence and dominance continue.'

'Your wish is my order, dear Father. I will do my best to live up to your expectations,' replied Jayanta.

An elaborate ceremony was arranged. The Devas were rejoicing, happy to get a new general. Amaravati was as bright as the sun. The mood was festive, everyone was happy and music blared. Just as a candle shines the brightest before being snuffed out, Amaravati was at its peak. No one except Jayanta and Indra were aware of the impending danger. After the ceremony, Jayanta gathered the key Devas and started strategizing the protection of Amaravati, without telling them everything his father had told him.

Indra, meanwhile, along with Agni and Vayu, his most trusted allies and warriors, started to plan the mass exodus of women and children from Amaravati to safety, having shared all he knew with them. They then left to their respective kingdoms to bolster themselves.

Sura

*H*aving let out a deafening war cry that echoed across the universe, the Asuras paraded from their yagnashala, marching northwards to meet their father, Kashyapa.

'Children! Your father had already ordered you to meet guru Sukhracharya and take his guidance. Obey him, Sura! Do not disturb your father from his meditation and anger him. He has asked me to accompany you all,' said Surasai.

On hearing these words, all of them marched towards Sukhra's ashram, led by the invincible Sura. On reaching the ashram, Surasai prostrated herself at the feet of Sukhra. Seeing their mother, the Asura clan followed suit. Sukhra was elated. Knowing that he would finally be able to avenge the injustice done to the Asuras by the vile Devas and scheming Vishnu, gave him immense joy.

'Rise, my children!' said Sukhra. 'Let this be the last time you fall at anyone's feet. It is not your destiny to fall at anyone's feet, except that of Parameswara. The rest of his creation will now fall at your feet. It will fall at the feet of my Asura clan, at the feet of invincible and unparalleled Sura!'

Sukhra gestured Surapadma, Tarakasura, Simhamukha, Ajamukhi and Surasai to follow him into his ashram, asking the rest to wait outside. He sat on his teacher's mound and asked the rest of them to sit down as well.

'Irrespective of merits or sin, my children, we will all eventually reach the feet of Shiva. All of us are his children. Our actions, irrespective of good or bad, have little impact on our ultimate end. Parameswara himself has given you the authority to rule the multiverse on his behalf. Rule it well. But remember, the Devas are our sworn enemies. Ask your mother, my children. Ask her about the humiliation we had to suffer due to the wretched Devas. Never forgive them. We need to punish them for eternity, to avenge every single humiliation. Be wary of Vishnu as well. He is not only cunning and powerful, but he is also dear to Mahadeva. Do not incur Mahadeva's wrath by disrespecting Vishnu. He will not come to the aid of the Devas, for he knows too well that but for Mahadeva's power, nothing can touch you, let alone defeat or slay you. The multiverse is yours to take. All creation is waiting to fall at your feet. Always worship Shiva and live as you please, my dear Asuras.

'Ajamukhi, Taraka and Simhamukha, never forsake your brother. His word is your destiny. Jump into fire if your elder brother orders so. Never fight with each other for anything. There is more joy in sacrificing for your brothers than in fighting for any material desire. Obey him. Counsel him if he needs it, but ultimately obey him.

'Sura, you are the emperor. The Asuras have been tortured by the Devas for yugas now. Return the favour to the Devas. Forgive your brothers if they make mistakes. An elder brother is akin to a father. He should guide his siblings, be there for them and support them without question. Whatever affects your siblings today will affect you tomorrow if no action is taken. Listen to their counsel as well, for they have nothing but the best of intentions for you. Their well-being is tied to yours, as yours is to them. Always be united: be united in taking over the multiverse, be united in ruling the multiverse, be united in avenging the Asuras and be united in life and in death.

'May the Asuras prosper under your rule! Jai Vijay Bhava!' said Sukhra.

'Only after our death, O esteemed guru, will anyone be able to even think of harming our brother,' said Simhamukha and Tarakasura in unison.

'I will always obey my three brothers, guru!' vowed Ajamukhi.

'I will follow every single word of your advice, mahaguru! I will avenge the Asuras. The Devas will be treated as they deserve to be. I will also take good care of my brothers,' replied Surapadma.

All of them took leave of their guru, after he taught them a few mantras that enabled them to travel faster than the wind, along with the original mantras he taught them, which helped them beat fatigue, hunger and sleep.

Sura came out and addressed his army of Asuras. They all cheered on hearing of their military campaign against the Devas and vowed to lay down their lives at the mere word of their new ruler, Surapadma!

Yuddha

Sura stamped his foot hard on the ground and shouted a war cry praising the Asuras. At the same moment, Indra's Vimana, or flying chariot, took off from Amaravati before the eyes of the Devas, Jayanta and Indra. This was considered to be a bad omen. The Devas knew and were proud of the fact that the Vimana had always and would always carry the most powerful ruler in the universe. It had served none except Daksha and Indra since coming into existence from the churning of the ocean. Being a sentient being, flying off by itself was a very bad omen. The Devas looked up at Jayanta's face, which expressed great worry at their impending fate.

The Vimana landed before Sura, who ascended it authoritatively. Sukhra smiled in contentment. Surasai was happy. Atisuran was proud of his grandson. If anyone still had any doubts about who the most powerful ruler in the universe at that moment was, it had been dispelled. Simhamukha and Tarakasura also took to their chariots pulled by hundreds of horses as they started to march in different directions with the sole aim of enslaving the king, the kingdom and the people under one Asura flag. They were followed by lakhs of soldiers, which included the Asuras born of Kashyapa's sweat, the Asura army of Atisuran and other clans who were sworn enemies of the Devas and were waiting for revenge. Through the blessings and power given to the Asura brothers by the grace of Shiva, the Asuras opened portals to other universes, not limiting their journey to the current one. By this time, the news of the Asura onslaught, their might and the boons they had obtained through hard and long penance, had spread far and wide.

Sura marched towards Alakapuri first. It was the land of Kubera, the wealthiest man in the universe. Gold is the first requirement for any army which aims to conduct a successful campaign against any enemy. It weakens the might of the enemy, strengthens the loyalty of the soldiers and helps build countries. As Sura entered the gates of Alakapuri through a portal, he was welcomed as the supreme emperor by Kubera himself. Kubera offered everything he had and would have to the Asura, accepting his supremacy and surrendering his sovereignty.

'O great Sura! The bravest warrior! King of kings! Ruler of the multiverse! Kindly accept this poor man's offering. I offer all the wealth I earned and will earn to you. I surrender my kingdom to you and seek your protection. My wives, children, subjects and I are nothing more than mere slaves of thine, O benevolent soul!' said Kubera, falling at the feet of Sura.

Sura laughed heartily. 'I would have believed you, had you maintained a friendly relationship with my grandfather when we were down on our fortune, Kubera. Shame on you! I can respect an enemy who fights me to death. I can respect a person who would rather die than bow to me out of fear. I cannot respect spineless cowards like you, who bend in the direction that the wind blows. You are fickle-minded and cannot be trusted,' thundered the mighty Asura.

'My only regret in all of this is that I am going to destroy a kingdom so beautifully built,' said Sura as he motioned his army to ravage the city and take everything. 'The only reason I will let you live, Kubera, is because you are a coward and killing a coward is so shameful an act that no Asura would ever do it,' he said as they left the kingdom. Alakapuri, the beautiful city, no longer lived up to its name: it was ravaged and ruined. Kubera cried as he saw his kingdom razed to the ground, his women taken and his men maimed.

The Asura army led by Sura moved east and came across Esanan, an aspect of Shiva. He had three eyes and could easily pass for Shiva himself, though he was nowhere near him in power. As soon as Sura laid eyes on him, he was told by Atisura's general who Esanan was. Sura folded his hands and prayed to Esanan, who reciprocated the respect he was offered, aware that the Asura was a staunch devotee of Shiva.

Sura then opened a portal to travel to his ultimate destination. He turned to his army as he told them that they were going to Amaravati. 'Spare no one, not even a child that has been just born or its mother. Every single Deva who exists or will exist is a threat and an enemy. The only good Devas are the dead ones or the ones in our prison. Kill whoever you can. If they do not die, since the Devas who drank Amrut cannot be killed except by Mahadeva at the end of time, maim them and arrest them. Their limbs will grow back. Do not be alarmed. Even lizards grow their tails back. The more Devas you kill or arrest, the higher the reward and position you will get from me,' said Sura.

As the mighty Sura's army entered Amaravati, he was welcomed by Jayanta. 'Who are you? Where is Indra?' raged Sura.

'I am Jayanta, son of Indra. He is not here. I am the general of the Devas, standing here to fight you and fight you I shall, till my last breath,' replied Jayanta.

'The coward Indra!' thundered Sura as war broke out. As anticipated, the Devas were no match for Sura and his army. Jayanta fought valiantly. The rest of the Devas, however, scrambled away as quickly as they could. Indra had gone into hiding, taking his wife and as many women and children he could with him. However, upon hearing the news of how badly they were faring, Indra abandoned them and ran away.

Jayanta lost his arms and legs. He fought until he could fight no more. Sura was impressed and respected him. 'Jayanta! I cannot believe that you are the son of Indra. Your bravery, fearlessness and courage rival the Asuras. If you had not been a Deva, you would be my general now. You will be treated well and with the respect that you have earned, even though you are our prisoner,' said Sura.

'No, I will not accept any special treatment. Treat me as you would treat any Deva, for I will fight you again once I get my arms and legs back,' replied Jayanta. With a heavy heart, Sura imprisoned Jayanta and the captured Devas. Whichever Deva he could not kill was made to carry the wealth from Amaravati and march behind the mighty Asura army.

Meanwhile, Tarakasura ventured into a different part of the universe, the one where Agni's kingdom was reigning. Agni took his fiercest form. His general Jwala was as fearless and as tough a woman that ever existed, barring the aspects of Shakti. Indeed, she was believed to be a manifestation of Shakti. Jwala and Agni fought so valiantly that some of the Asuras started to fear defeat. Seeing the morale of his army being tested, Tarakasura took out the Pasupatastra, the divine Astra given to him by Shiva. This Astra could raze kingdoms and, seeing it, Agni knew that the war was over. He wanted to save the lives of his people and kingdom rather than let it burn down by his foolhardiness.

Agni toned down from his fiercest form and stood before

Tarakasura. Jwala followed her king.

'Taraka! Do not destroy my people and kingdom. The Astra you have can destroy universes. I do not want my kingdom burned down with all my innocent subjects. I offer my life to you first. In return, spare my people,' said Agni.

'O noble Deva! You fought bravely, unlike Kubera or Indra. You have earned my respect. I promise you that I will neither harm you nor will I harm your people, so long as you accept my sovereignty and come whenever we beckon. You are free to continue to rule your kingdom as you did before, except when we need you,' said Tarakasura kindly.

'Thank you, noble Asura for sparing the life of my subjects. I give you my word and accept your sovereignty. I will bow before none but you brothers and Trimurti,' said Agni.

On another front, Yamaloka was being targeted by Simhamukha. Yamadharmaraja fought valiantly, impressing Simhamukha. When asked to surrender, Yama said that he always followed his duty and has never slipped from it, except on the orders of Mahadeva. Hearing Mahadeva's name and respecting Yama's dutifulness, Simhamukha also let Yamaloka be, extracting the promise that Yama would always inform the Asura brothers before taking anyone's life.

Next, Simhamukha proceeded to Satyaloka, the residence of Brahma, who knew what was coming and welcomed Simhamukha. He offered his Brahmastra and other divine Astras as gifts to Simhamukha. Whether Simhamukha liked it or not, Brahma was his great grandfather on his paternal side. He accepted the gift, took his blessings and left. He also informed Brahma that since the Asuras have now taken over the multiverse, Brahma too would be their subject and would come to them to officiate any and every function as and when the Asuras wanted it. He assured Brahma that he would be treated with respect as a great grandfather but would still be treated as a subject when the need comes. Brahma acknowledged his understanding of the situation to Simhamukha.

After this, Simhamukha met Vayu and Varuna, who surrendered meekly like Kubera.

Mahavishnu

*T*arakasura then proceeded to open a portal to Vaikunta. Seeing the approaching army, Lakshmi ran to Vishnu, who was in anantasayana on Adishesha. As Lakshmi woke him up, Vishnu smiled and said, 'I know, my dear. I will take care of it as always. Take residence in my heart and nothing shall ever harm you.'

'The Asuras have destroyed Amaravati, Yamaloka, Agniloka, Alakapuri and Varunaloka. They took over all the places without getting a single scratch. They are invincible. I am told by Narada that nothing and no one but Mahadeva can defeat them. How will you manage?' asked Lakshmi.

Vishnu replied with a smile, 'They are not the only invincible ones, Lakshmi. The boon that Mahadeva gave them only means that I cannot defeat them. It does not mean that they can defeat me. Besides, anyone who is dear to Mahadeva is dear to me. He and I are one and the same. I will also test them and then bless them. Do not fear, my dear. I will take care of this.'

Lakshmi entered Vishnu's heart and took residence there. She was safe from harm; she knew that for sure. Vishnu, the Paramatma, the protector of Dharma, was prepared: no one had killed more Asuras in combat than him.

Tarakasura was well aware of what he was getting into. He decided to proceed, knowing that everyone understood that no one could save them. He also knew that dying at the hands of the Paramatma was also not going to happen, thanks to the boons from Shiva. It was most likely going to be a stalemate. However, even a stalemate was victory, as no one would run and seek refuge at the feet of Vishnu.

Mahavishnu blew the Panchajanya, his conch, and it echoed across the universe, declaring war on Tarakasura. A war like no other broke out. Thousands and thousands of Asuras died, unable to bear the power of the divine Astras coming from Sarangai, the bow of Vishnu. None of the Astras that Tarakasura used seemed to deter Mahavishnu either. The war continued for centuries with no result.

In desperation, Tarakasura took out the Pasupatastra. He then remembered his guru's words, that Vishnu was dear to Mahadeva, and if Shiva came to know that Taraka had attempted to use the Pasupatastra on Vishnu, he would be burnt to ashes immediately. He hesitated and put away the Astra. Vishnu then proceeded to take out the Sudarshan Chakra, a serrated discus that spewed fire in all directions and cut everything in its path before returning to Mahavishnu. It was the ultimate weapon in Vishnu's arsenal and he had slain many a great Asura using this weapon.

Seeing the Chakra, the Asura army ran helter-skelter. They believed that they were doomed. Upon seeing this and realizing that only he had been blessed by Shiva and not his entire army, Tarakasura immediately took a giant form to shield his army.

Vishnu cast the Sudarshan Chakra, aiming for Tarakasura's chest. Having no choice or counter, Tarakasura stood bravely and took the brunt of the serrations ravaging his chest. Mahavishnu was immensely impressed by the courage and bravery exhibited by the Asura.

'O brave Asura! You and your brothers deserve all the boons given by Mahadeva. Not only are you devout but are also brave. As a sign of how bravely you fought against me, let the Sudarshan Chakra that I cast on you be embedded in your chest. Let it be a medal granted to you by my blessings, a medal acknowledging your bravery in times of adversity,' said Mahavishnu.

Tarakasura replied, 'O great lord! I have only heard about your cunning. Having witnessed your prowess and grace at the same time, I understand why you are so revered, respected and loved by one and all, right up to the supreme lord Mahadeva. Please bless me.'

'May you live long and prosper. There will never be any want for anything ever in your kingdom. The Lakshmi living in my heart will bless your kingdom, ensuring prosperity, peace and abundance, so long as the Chakra is embedded in your chest, until your time comes. The Chakra will fall off your chest only if you remove it of your own free will,' blessed Vishnu.

The elephant-headed Asura took leave of the great god as a grown and humble Asura.

Indra and the rest of the Devas, or what was left of them, ran to Mahavishnu. They saw him as the last resort, as Mahadeva was unapproachable in the current circumstances. They did not have the time or patience for penance either. Vishnu was in anantasayana, looking across universes to see how things were proceeding.

'O Paramatma! Paraman has forsaken us. Have you done the same as well? We were hoping against hope that you would defeat Tarakasura and help check the Asura onslaught. However, you blessed them. Please tell us how and when we will get out of our predicament. When will we see our honour restored?' asked Indra.

Vishnu woke up with a smile. 'O Indra! Have you forgotten that you and the Devas chose to attend the yagna of Daksha even though the sole aim of it was to insult Mahadeva! Brahma and I advised you and the Devas against it. You are paying the price for your actions. Though the two of us went to the yagna with the intention of persuading Daksha not to proceed, we could not succeed. Our intention was overshadowed by our attendance. Your attendance and intention, however, were not straight, Sakra. You and the Devas will pay the price. Nandi's curse has come to fruition,' replied Mahavishnu.

'Will there be an end? Is our sin unforgivable?' asked Indra.

'This too shall change, O Sakra, as all else will. Shiva's Shakti, in form of his offspring alone, will destroy the Asuras when the time is right. Until then, endure,' replied Mahavishnu.

'But Shiva is without a wife. Ever since Sati entered the fire, Shiva has not left his meditative trance, except for when he was invoked by the Asuras after millennia of penance. He has again gone back to teaching the Brahma Kumaras. Nandi is not letting anyone near Kailash, let alone a woman. How will he beget a son who will redeem us? Please help us, O Idhayakamalavasa!'

'I have told you how you will be redeemed, Sakra. When and where is something that has to be left to time and karma,' replied Mahavishnu. He then slipped back into his yoganidra, leaving the Devas led by Indra to their own devices.

Veeramahendrapuri

*E*veryone who could have been a major challenge to Asura supremacy was conquered and the rest acquiesced and accepted the valiant Asura Sura as their emperor. He had fulfilled his mother's dream and his guru's order. Having established themselves as the ruler of the multiverse by defeating all the other rulers, either through conquest or by making them submit through threat, the three Asura brothers decided to establish their own independent kingdoms to manage and control their subjects.

Tarakasura chose the beautiful Vindhya mountains, where they had met Krauncha, as his abode. He got Vishwakarma to build a beautiful palace that occupied the entire area of Amaravati and called it Mayapuri. He took an Asura wife, Savurika, and made her the queen. He also proceeded to take any and every Deva woman he could find as his concubine. Some of them surrendered out of fear for their lives while the others gave in to ensure the safety of their children. He got some of the captured Devas to perform menial labour and made sure to torment them whenever and wherever possible. He also allowed the privilege of taking Devas as slaves and abusing them to any Asura who was powerful and useful in running his kingdom. Krauncha held a special place in his heart as a friend and was given special privileges as well as respect as befits a king.

Simhamukha followed suit and established an island kingdom for himself, which he called Asurapuri. He took Yama's daughter, Vibhuti, for his wife. He was a Shakti devotee who worshipped her as Kali, the most fearsome, destructive and powerful aspect of Shakti. He was the kindest of the Asura brothers, who treated Devas with respect, even though they were second-class citizens in Asurapuri. He also treated the Deva womenfolk merely as servants instead of as slaves or concubines, unless they were willing and consented to be his. The Devas still lamented their misfortune but were grateful that they were in Asurapuri as opposed to Mayapuri, or worse, Veeramahendrapuri.

Surapadma ruled from Veeramahendrapuri. Unlike his brothers, he was not content with getting his now father-in-law, Vishwakarma, to construct an elaborate fortress and a palace. He wanted more. He, after all, was the master of the multiverse. Everyone bowed to him, whether they liked it or not. He flew in the Vimana and chose a location in the middle of the ocean, where he ordered Varuna, the god of water, and the ocean's guardian deity, Samudra, to elevate and create a landmass twice as big as Amaravati, the erstwhile most beautiful city in the universe. They did not have a choice and obeyed him.

Once the landmass came into being, he tasked his father-in-law to build a city entirely out of gold bricks. He ordered Kubera to supply the gold and asked the Gandharvas, who could fly, to act as courier to get the gold to Vishwakarma. The whole city, made of gold, had no doors and there was no need for one either. Fear was not something known to a resident of the city. The city was named intentionally: Veera meant fearless, Maha meant great, Indra meant ruler of universe and Puri meant residence. It was the residence of the fearless great ruler of the multiverse, Surapadma.

There was a centralized kitchen in the city manned by Devas, whose task was to cook for all the residents. The residents were handpicked by the Asura himself to ensure that the highest quality of progeny continued in Veeramahendrapuri. The bravest and handsomest of Asura alone could become residents. The most beautiful women from all races were taken into the city as wives, concubines and slaves, depending upon which race they belonged to.

Around Veeramahendrapuri, arranged in concentric circles, there were seven islands, all of them artificially elevated and built by Vishwakarma as impregnable fortresses guarded by the best Asuras. They even had the seventh circle filled with Rakshasas, a cannibalistic man-flesh-eating race known for its unmatched strength, anger and foolhardiness. Residence in each of the concentric circles around the valiant Asura's city was granted based on the person meeting specific criteria set to evaluate their ability and need.

At sunrise, when and if Sura allowed it, the city shone so bright that one could see its beauty from hundreds of thousands of miles away. It seemed as if the city was on fire. At the heart of the city was the Asura's palace. If only words had the power to describe its beauty! It had the most beautiful garden, filled with colourful aromatic flowers, and also housed the Kalpakavriksha, which had the power to grant any wish one sought from it. Airavata, the divine white flying elephant of Indra, and Kamadhenu, the divine cow that can grant any wish, now roamed in the garden. The Parijat tree, capable of blossoming beautiful flowers, was the centrepiece. Its fragrance was divine and filled the entire city. All the golden deer from Mana Sarovar, which the lake in Veeramahendrapuri palace was made to resemble, roamed around and played among the flowers. Beautiful birds, butterflies and bees floated and flew around the garden. Beautiful swans now made the lake in the palace their home.

The palace itself was divine. The bedroom of the emperor was by the lake and Chandra, the moon god, was tasked with lighting the room every night with a full moon. Beautiful fish of all colours jumped and played around the still lake by the palace. The golden pillars of the bedroom were adorned by lush green creepers which flowered beautifully every day and night.

The regal throne, which had once seated Daksha and Indra, now stayed in the courtroom in Veeramahendrapuri. The courtroom had enough space to accommodate all of the residents of the city, if required. There were five more seats as high and as big as the throne, placed by the side, three for Sura's siblings, one for his mother and one for his guru, Sukhra. There was also an additional seat, a bit smaller, meant for the emperor's invited guest. The rest of those present were to stand and conduct their business in the room, whatever it was.

The paternal great grandfather of the Asuras, Brahma, crowned Surapadma as the supreme ruler of the multiverse on an auspicious day. On the same day, Surapadma married Padumakomalai, the daughter of Vishwakarma; Brahma again acted as master of ceremonies. Vishnu attended the ceremony as a witness and was treated with due respect and sat in the guest's seat. He too left as soon as the crowning was over. They dared not disturb Shiva, who was still engaged in educating the Kumaras, as Nandi forbade them to enter, even to invite him.

'None other than an Asura will ever enter the palace but as a slave henceforth. No Asura other than one as mighty as the children of Maya will get a seat in this court room,' thundered Surapadma as his first order, as soon as he was crowned. He turned proudly to look at his siblings, Ajamukhi, Tarakasura and Simhamukha, who nodded in agreement.

The faces of Sukhra, Surasai and Asurendran, who took the

guest seat after the coronation, beamed with pride. Sukhra said, 'O mighty Asura! From now until forever, may you reign supreme. Remember everything I taught you. Listen to your mother. Stay united. Never underestimate the Devas or Vishnu. Never ignore the worship of Parameswara, for without his grace, none of this would have been possible.' The Asura siblings bowed to their guru as he took their leave.

They then proceeded to seek the blessings of their mother and their maternal grandfather, who blessed them in unison. Atisuran turned to Surasai and said, 'My dear daughter! You have accomplished what generations of Asuras have tried and failed. You have succeeded in raising the banner of the Asuras high. You deserve all the credit, my child. I am proud that I can call myself your father, Surasai and your grandfather, my children.'

Surasai replied, 'O dear father, all the credit goes to our esteemed guru, who planned everything and executed it at the right time. I was merely a pawn in his plan, as my children were. It is time now father, children, for us to unleash our vengeance upon the Devas.'

She then turned to her children and said, 'The Devas might be thinking that the defeat at your hands, my sons, was the worst thing that could happen to them. Prove them wrong, my children. Take vengeance for every single insult, betrayal and backstabbing we as a race had to endure at the hands of the Devas. They extracted our work during the churning of the ocean and denied us the benefits. The Amrut was supposed to be shared between us for the work we put in. The same Amrut that made the Devas immortal should also have made us immortal. We may be forced to spare Vishnu, who was behind all this, but we still have the Devas on whom we can wreak havoc. Spare no one. Waste not a moment that could be spent punishing the Devas, my children.'

Shraap

Surapadma's palace was entirely staffed with the elite of the enslaved Devas. In the palace, Vayu, the god of wind, was the one in charge of ventilation and cleanliness. He was tasked with ensuring that the streets were swept clean in all seven islands using wind. He also personally had to fan the Asura himself wherever he went. Surya and Chandra had the task of illuminating the palace according to the mood of the Asura. There was no system or rule: they simply had to ask him and follow his orders. Varuna, the god of rain and water, had to take care of the garden. He had to provide water and tend to the flowers and plants, gather fruits and remove weeds. Kubera, who once was the richest man in the universe and had a purse that would never be empty, now held the spittoon of the Asura, along with the betel leaf and nut purse. They were thrashed by Sura himself whenever he felt like doing so. If the elite had to endure the ignominy of being treated like slaves and given menial tasks, the torture that the second rung of Devas had to endure in Veeramahendrapuri was unimaginably painful.

In the second island, there was an elaborate prison setup, with exclusive torture chambers meant for the Devas. This was where the Devas who were led by Jayanta, were held prisoner. Jayanta, even though he was a slave as well, was treated better than his fellow Devas. However, he chose to stay with and endure the same treatment as the people who fought with him were subjected to.

As soon as the Asuras found out that the Devas could grow back their limbs, their bodies were cut into pieces for fun by the Asuras and their children. They were used as food to feed the cannibalistic Rakshasa army that lived in the seventh circle. They were also used as gladiators' victims as well, but the worst of all was the research and experimentation carried out on them.

The body parts were cut up and researched to see the source

of immortal life. It was something that the Devas had and the Asuras could never have, unless granted by Parameswara as a boon. Surapadma wanted a way to extract Amrut from their body and use the same to grant immortality to his race. The captured Devas, barring Jayanta, who was untouchable thanks to the respect he had earned during the war with Sura, were subjected to numerous surgical procedures to find ways to kill them for good as well as to extract the source of their immortality.

As a routine, the Devas were numbered sequentially and selected for their attributes to conduct experiments. The tougher and stronger a Deva was, the more he was subjected to torture. The Devas did not need to blink, so their eyelids were torn off and eyes gouged out to find out if that was the source of their immortality. Their legs floated above the surface of the earth, so their legs were cut off to see if they still floated and if so, would the Asuras float if they were to be attached to a Deva's leg. Unfortunately, it didn't let Asuras float. The Devas' nails and teeth were as strong and pure as ivory, so their nails and teeth were pulled off with pincers and used to make toys for Asura children and jewellery for Asura men and women. The Devas had a glow about them, thanks to Amrut, so they were skinned alive for an Asura to wear the Deva skin and see if they could glow. Numerous combinations of Deva body parts were used to recreate an Asura equal to a Deva in terms of his physical attribute, which was believed to be the source of their immortality. Even the Deva hearts and brains were not spared.

The Devas were burnt alive for months to see if they still returned to their original form at the end of it. They were submerged in various acids to see if that would be enough to destroy them. The Devas, though immortal, were not immune to pain. Their screams, while they were subjected to numerous tortures, pushed Jayanta to madness and the Asuras to ecstasy. Jayanta's situation was made worse by the fact that all he could do was sit helplessly and hear other Devas scream. He begged the Asuras to take him and subject him to the same torture as the rest of them, so that he could at least show his comrades that he too was willing and was experiencing the same pain as them, thereby understanding their pain. He was denied the request summarily. There was no way he could end his life: he wanted to do it many a times, but his immortality as a Deva was both a curse and a gift.

Jayanta worshipped Mahadeva to put an end to the misery of the Devas or put an end to his existence. He, after all, had not attended the Daksha yagna. He had not committed a mistake to merit this torture. Mahadeva, however, was otherwise engaged. Jayanta's father had forsaken him, and there was no end in sight for the might of Sura, and having witnessed his power first-hand, it made him feel hopeless.

The Deva womenfolk were made available as prostitutes to any and every Asura in the vicinity. They were raped at will and their children were used as playthings for Asura children to have fun with. The Asura womenfolk were not kind either. After all, they had seen their husbands being subjected to abject defeat and humiliation at the hands of the Devas for centuries. Add to that the jealousy they felt when their husbands went with Deva women and the result was not too pleasant. On good or auspicious days, the Asura women skinned the Deva women alive and used their glowing skin as articles of clothing.

Veeramahendrapuri was to the Devas what hell was to the worst of sinners. Mayapuri was the second circle of hell where torture was not as organized as in Veeramahendrapuri, but was painful, random, erratic and arduous, nonetheless.

'Don't fear. Feel solace in knowing that Indra, our king, is out there somewhere planning something and there will be an end to all this one day. So long as he is out and safe, we still have a chance, a glimmer of hope as small as it is. Nandi's curse has hit home. Father can and will win back favour as well as freedom from Nandi's curse by worshipping Mahadeva,' said Jayanta to whichever Deva he could talk to, whenever he could.

Hope

*J*ayanta was walking to and fro in his cell. There was nothing else to do. The screams of the Devas being tortured had settled down for the day. It was also an auspicious day in Veeramahendrapuri. A prince had been born to Surapadma and Padumakomalai. All the guards, barring a couple of them, had left for the main island to attend the celebrations. The last time they had got such a break was when Asurendran was born to Tarakasura and his wife.

Suddenly, a butterfly flew into Jayanta's cell. He felt immense gratitude, considering that it had been decades since he had last seen the sun, moon, flowers or the sun god or moon god.

'How did you get in here? This place is not meant for creatures like you. There is no flower to give you honey. Go away before an Asura swats you,' said Jayanta, smiling for the first time in a long time at the thought of having company that bore no ill will.

The butterfly flitted around and settled down on the wall. Slowly it transformed into a humanoid form, eventually taking the shape of Indra, to Jayanta's surprise.

'Father!' cried Jayanta in joy and relief. 'How did you manage to get past all the security across the islands? Why did you come here, Father? If they see you, they will subject you to unspeakable horrors!' cried Jayanta as his joy quickly turned into worry.

'Don't worry, my son,' said Indra. 'I have come thus far without getting caught. I will also find a way out in the same manner. I have come bearing good news. I have found a way to please Mahadeva and got him to restore us to our old glory. He has given me great boons and we will now take back what is rightfully ours. I want you to rally the Devas, give them hope and get them ready. The celebrations are on for a week, the guards will be lax. I have come with our Vimana, which is below the hill on this island. There are only five or six guards till there. Take this flower and place it on their nostrils. They will faint. Come quickly and quietly. Don't risk fighting the guards. We do not want to raise an alarm as we must cross six islands to make sure we are safe from the clutches of Sura. We will then rally the forces and attack when the time is ripe. We will start with Tarakasura,' Indra finished.

'Yes Father, I will do as you command. I will get the Devas to the hill and then we can go out. Once we are out, we will take care of the Asuras. O Father! I thought that I would never get to see this day,' said Jayanta.

'Keep your head low and morale high, my son. Victory shall be ours!' said Indra, as he turned back into a butterfly and flew out of the cell.

Jayanta quickly took the flower and used it on the Asura guarding his cell, easing him down gently, not letting him fall over. He was housed in the lowest floor of the dungeon, facing the torture chamber. Using all possible stealth, he took the keys off the Asura and went out of his cell. He then proceeded to see where the next Asura guard was standing. He quietly freed the Devas in the nearby cells and they quietly proceeded to the next higher floor. They had to go five more flights to reach the surface of the earth.

At each level, the guards were scant and those who were there fell easily. It was the perfect time. Like Jayanta had always hoped, his father had come to their rescue. The Devas breathed easy, filled with hope for the first time in what felt like and could possibly be centuries.

They slowly ascended, following Jayanta's instructions diligently. They climbed higher and higher. A couple more floors and they would get to see the sky after a long time. A few of the Devas could not accompany them as their limbs had been torn off or mutilated. A few others refused to come, having given up all hope. Those who still retained a fighting spirit accompanied Jayanta. They reached the top floor after taking out the final guard and finally saw the sky. Jayanta rallied them towards the hill as quickly and quietly as possible. They could not see a single guard but could hear loud celebrations, music and Rudram being chanted. There was a huge prayer going on, praising Lord Shiva and thanking him for giving them a prince.

At the sight of Indra standing near the Vimana, any doubts that the Devas and Jayanta had about their escape plan were removed. They felt joy for the first time as they ran towards the Vimana. Jayanta hugged his father and the Devas paid their respects. Indra acknowledged the Devas as he hugged his son and then asked them to board the Vimana.

The Vimana started to take off and the Devas finally felt elation at the thought of being free, more than anything else. The horrendous torture they had been subjected to was over for them. Even if they could not gain their old status back, even if they had to live as fugitives for eternity, it would be better than what they were being subjected to at the hands of the evil Asuras. They all sat down, relaxed, as the Vimana soared into the sky.

The Vimana, however, turned towards Veeramahendrapuri.

Confrontation

*J*ayanta turned towards his father, the king and leader of the Devas, shocked. All he could see from behind was his father's flowing golden hair. The Devas were equally confused but completely trusted Indra, their king, and Jayanta, their general. They did not question either of them. Jayanta rushed to the front where Indra was standing, but hesitated to question his father. He had always looked up to him and trusted him implicitly, even when his father had forsaken him to fight the war against Surapadma all by himself.

'Father, why are we going towards Veeramahendrapuri?' asked Jayanta in a low voice without the slightest hint of disrespect. 'You will see,' came the reply from Indra, who did not even turn around.

Jayanta and the Devas were confused about what their leader could be thinking. Was there a plan to go and attack Surapadma directly and destroy him one on one in his bedroom, with the Devas and Jayanta taking care of the guards? After all, Sura was not immortal like Indra and Indra now had the blessings and boons of Parameswara himself. That must be it, they thought to themselves. But it was afternoon. They should have hidden in the island under the hill till it was night for the plan. Even if that was the plan, why did their leader not take anyone into his confidence? Even if the Devas were not worthy of Indra to share his plans with, Jayanta, their general, was. That was it, believed the Devas, Indra would have shared his plan with Jayanta. They all turned to Jayanta and were flabbergasted to see him as confused as they were.

As soon as the Vimana entered the outskirts of Veeramahendrapuri, Jayanta and the Devas could not help themselves but admire the beauty of the city. Until that moment, they had believed that Amaravati was and forever would be unrivalled when it came to beauty, functionality and efficiency. This city was the very definition of all three: it should be retained and used once they came back to power, hoped the Devas.

However, as they entered the inner city over Surapadma's palace, they were reminded of their current state. Jayanta was especially heartbroken when he saw Airavata, Kalpakavriksha and Kamadhenu, and smelled the sweet scent of the divine Parijat flower that once filled the air in Amaravati. He felt pangs of pain as he was reminded of the past when they had been the rulers and had little to nothing to worry about. Falling from such a high place to such a low position as they were currently in was worse than death. Death also could not save them, thanks to the accursed Amrut. Jayanta lamented the day when then Devas had chosen to go after Amrut.

The Vimana landed right in the middle of a colosseum-like structure and they were surrounded by hundreds of thousands of Asuras in broad daylight. Indra alighted from the Vimana and asked the Devas led by Jayanta to do the same. The Vimana took off as soon as they alighted.

The Devas looked around and saw the Asuras angry at the mere sight of Indra and the Devas. They, however, maintained decorum as they were ordered to. In the royal enclosure, there were four empty thrones in front with a few seats at the back.

Ajamukhi's name was announced first, and she came in and took a throne. She was followed by Tarakasura, with a long list of adjectives preceding his name. He came in and sat on one of the thrones as the whole crowd cheered. As the Devas and Asuras in there expected, the next person who came in was Simhamukha, who was cheered even louder. He came in without any pomp. As soon as Simhamukha came in, Indra started flying towards the royal seat, leaving Jayanta and the Devas stunned. They did not know that their king could fly, for one. Even if it was one of Shiva's boons, it would be foolish to fly towards certain defeat, something uncharacteristic of Indra.

The Asuras let out a huge cry. The three Sura siblings were however cool and smiling as they saw Indra soar towards them. He landed in the royal enclosure as Surapadma's name was announced, and took out his Vajrayudha, the lightning bolt that Indra used, to destroy Vritra. He turned around and laughed out loud. This angered the crowd even more. He then slowly transformed into Surapadma, much to the audience's astonishment and the Devas' despair.

The three Sura siblings joined Surapadma in his laughter. Jayanta was boiling with rage. The rest of the Devas were desolate.

They had been taken for a ride. What was worse was that Sura now knew who among the Devas still held hope and were willing to fight, which would mean even more torture.

'O brave Jayanta! I wanted to invite you to the celebrations on account of the birth of my son, the future scion of the Asura empire. You would have declined. I also wanted you to see what kind of coward your father really was, lest you and your fellow Devas were harbouring hope that he would somehow find a way to rescue you. Further, I wanted my brothers and sister to see why I hold you in such high esteem. Additionally, I wanted to dash any hopes you or the Devas might have of redemption from your current predicament. Hence, the whole scene,' said the Asura as his wife Padumakomalai came in with Banugopan, their son, who was playing with something shiny and round in his hands, which caught Jayanta's attention. Sura noticed the disbelief on Jayanta's face when he realized what it was.

'Yes Jayanta. You are right. He is my son, Banugopan, the one who plays with the sun. The shiny round object he is fearlessly playing with is the sun, your sun,' said the Asura, as if he had read Jayanta's mind.

Jayanta had completely lost any semblance of sanity at this point. He was not merely humiliated but was humiliated in front of the entire Asura race who hated him and in front of his fellow Devas who, until this point, looked towards him with hope. He had been telling them day in and out that their leader and king would come to rescue them. He could no longer do that, for he no longer believed that.

'Indra, your father, was last seen in a forest near Amaravati. He has gone into hiding, leaving behind all the women and children he was supposed to protect from us. He even dropped the Vajrayudha which serves me well. They scattered all over the place and were caught in time. We did not care much about them though. We only want Indra and his wife, Indrani, your mother,' said the Asura again, as if reading Jayanta's mind.

At the mere mention of his mother, Jayanta let out a loud cry that silenced the whole crowd of Asuras for a second. 'See, my brothers!' said Sura. 'He is a captive, surrounded by the best Asuras, standing in front of the rulers of the multiverse and yet, he is fearless. Now you know where my respect for him stems from.'

'Send in the Rakshasas,' commanded Sura. A horde of Rakshasas, many times bigger than the Devas, came in. The Devas stood lifeless and hopeless. They would be swallowed whole by the Rakshasas, digested as much as possible and excreted, only to retain their own self again. They prayed and hoped desperately that they would not survive the digestion process to come back to this hell, this shameful place where they have been stripped of every single shred of dignity one could possibly have.

Jayanta jumped at them and tore the Rakshasas limb from limb, making short work of them. All his disillusionment and disappointment aimed at his father, Indra, his benefactor, Vishnu, and his god, Mahadeva, turned into rage as he tore the heads off the mighty gargantuan Rakshasas with his bare hands. Sura laughed in pride from the enclosure as the Asuras cheered at the sight of the carnage.

Then, he stood with his head down. 'You have broken me, my emperor,' said Jayanta as he looked at Sura. 'I bow to you. You have not only beaten my father, Devendra, in might and strategy but also in deceit and guile. I have only one request for you now and this shall be the last word I speak so long as I have no hope left. Spare my mother.'

Jayanta knelt with his head bowed. The rest of the Devas followed suit, as the Asuras in audience cheered and clapped.

'You will always have my respect, Jayanta. After your exhibition of might, courage, power and bravery, my brothers too now see you with the same respect that I have. You will be treated well, and you are free to walk out of the prison and join us as chief of the enslaved Devas whenever you see fit. If only your father or Surya or Vayu or Varuna had your courage and bravery, it would have made the conquest of this universe even more challenging,' said Sura.

'Take them away,' Sura signalled and they were taken back to the prison where they had come from.

Ajamukhi, Sura's beloved sister and the apple of her brother's eye, however, now had more than respect for Jayanta. She wanted him. Seeing him tear the giant Rakshasas apart with his bare hands had made the already lustful Ajamukhi covet Jayanta even more. She smiled at him amorously as he was being taken away. His head was bowed, though, and he no longer cared where he was or what happened to him.

Ajamukhi

*A*jamukhi was a typical spoilt child. With a face that resembled a goat, she had been born of pure lust between her father and mother. Unlike her brothers, she had absolutely no devotion to Mahadeva and did not get any boon or blessing from him. After her birth, she was pampered by her grandfather who brought her up and cherished as the apple of the three brothers' eyes. She was the second most powerful person in Asurapuri, Veeramahendrapuri and Mayapuri. The three brothers would never even dream of saying no to her, no matter what she asked for. Simhamukha was the only one who advised her now and then to mend her ways, but she paid no heed to him. All she ever asked for was sex. She had no inhibitions or restrictions as to what kind of creature she preferred. She did not have to, considering that her brothers ruled the entire spectrum of universes. If she wanted someone, she had them. Rishis, Gandharvas, Rakshasas, Asuras, Nagas, Devas, Vasus, Manushyas, animals—no one was spared. If she wanted them, they were hers. 'No' was something she had never heard in her life thus far.

Now, she wanted Jayanta. He was, after all, a slave now. He belonged to her already. She got ready and went to the island where Jayanta was held. Upon seeing her and her dreaded bodyguard, the Asuras bowed and escorted her to Jayanta's cell.

Jayanta, who now no longer held any hope, was quiet and lost. He was in an emotional void, lost deep within himself, no thoughts running through his head. A mere zombie when it came to emotions, Jayanta was no longer even bothered by the wailing and screaming of the Devas who were being tortured.

'Slave! The Asura princess is here to see you. Kneel!' yelled the guards as Ajamukhi entered the cell.

Jayanta did not even flinch. He couldn't hear anything. Sound entered his ear but did not reach his brain; visuals captured by his eyes were blocked away. The Asura guard hit him in the knee, and he knelt automatically, more as a reflex than as a conscious decision to combat pain. A slap rang across the room: the Asura who had hit Jayanta fell down bleeding and shivering in fear.

'Nobody touches him! He's mine and mine alone!' shouted Ajamukhi in a shrill voice. The fallen Asura scrambled away as quickly as he could, leaving the princess of Asuras and the prince of Devas alone.

'My dear! No one will hurt you, ever again,' Ajamukhi cajoled sweetly. 'Consent to be mine and I will ask my brother to give you complete freedom. He already respects you. If he knew that you are my lover, he will set you free, as he did many of your Devas, who now live in my harem with me. You will be totally free but for when I want you...'

Jayanta did not even move a muscle. He remained on his knees.

'Do not fear, Jayanta. You are my darling. You will be the chief among my consorts. You will be treated as befits a prince. You can get out of this hell and live in Veeramahendrapuri, Asurapuri or

Mayapuri as you choose. I have harems everywhere. You will be attended to by my Asura servants. You will be taken care of by my Asura women servants. You can have any and as many men, women or animals as you want. Somabhana flows in my harem. Drink as much as you want. Eat all you want and can. Whatever your heart's desire is, it will be given to you. All you must do is consent to be mine and fulfil my lust when I seek it. Think, Jayanta. The freedom that you thought you will never get will be yours. You will be free to roam anywhere in the three cities. You will be as free as an Asura is. Be mine, accept me, take this ring and this ring will be your pass to anywhere in the Asura kingdom. You will be treated as I would be,' Ajamukhi beseeched him as she knelt and came face to face with Jayanta.

Quick to anger at the lack of a response, Ajamukhi stood up and kicked Jayanta on his chest, felling him to the ground. Her coyness and sweet tone disappeared in an instant.

'Who do you think you are, Jayanta? You are merely a slave of the Asura clan for eternity. The audacity you must have to shun my advances! Do you think I cannot forcefully have you?' threatened Ajamukhi.

Jayanta was as blank as ever, and he remained in the fallen position.

Ajamukhi clapped her hands. Two Asuras scrambled in. 'Make him stand and strip him,' ordered Ajamukhi and they obliged. Jayanta, however, was dead inside: he did not even move a muscle to defend himself or fight back. Ajamukhi was irate.

'This is your last opportunity, Jayanta. If you do not concede to my command before I leave this chamber, you will regret this day for the rest of eternity. If you thought you were being tortured thus far, the things I will do to you will make everything you have been through so far seem like child's play. I will count to ten,' said Ajamukhi. She had never felt so humiliated: no one had ever made her ask twice. She ordered and got what she wanted.

'Ten, nine, eight, seven ... your time is running out, Jayanta. I will double the torture on the Devas. Six, five, four ... this will be your last chance at freedom. Three, two ... you will regret this, you vile arrogant miserly Deva! One. Leave him unclothed, double up the torture on the Devas. Make him watch the whole thing until he comes begging to me for my grace,' commanded Ajamukhi. Her loud angry voice was heard at all levels of the prison, but Jayanta did not even stir.

This drove Ajamukhi mad. All her lust now turned to hate. She now wanted to have him, even if it was merely to satisfy her massive ego. A thought stuck her: she tried to recollect his last words.

'Spare my mother,' she remembered. 'Your mother,' Ajamukhi said, laughing. 'My brother wants your mother and father. You do not care about your father any more. Your last words were "spare my mother". I will go after her. Your mother will pay for you insulting me. I will find her. I will make her the concubine of every single Asura. She will be repeatedly used and abused. You will pay, O vain Jayanta! Your mother will pay. She will curse the moment you were born to her. She will curse you and disown you for making her go through the hell that I have planned for her. I will go after her, find her, bring her here in front of you and then gift her to my brother.

'Then, I will get my brother to release her to me. I will gift her to the Rakshasas, Asuras, Danavas, Nagas, Gandharvas. Everyone will do to her what you refused to do with me. You, vain Deva, will see it with your own eyes. It will teach you a lesson for turning me down, for humiliating me. If this does not happen, I am not Kashyapa and Surasai's daughter, I am not Surapadma, Tarakasura and Simhamukha's sister. I will immediately send out all my guards to search for and bring your mother here. Until then, I will not adorn my hair,' yelled Ajamukhi as she let her hair loose and stormed out of the cell and off the island.

Jayanta did not stir. He was as dead as a Deva could possibly be.

Indra Parva

Indrani

*O*nce the reigning queen of the universe, now a fugitive running from the Asuras, Indrani was still poised. She had unshakeable faith in Mahadeva, the supreme lord. She understood that what she was going through was due to karma. She never questioned the lord at times of trouble, knowing that the lord knows what to give, when to give, whom to give, how to give, where to give and that which is to be given.

She still believed that her husband, who it may seem had abandoned her, was doing everything he possibly could. She was not disappointed him because she never saw him as the invincible king of the Devas. To her, he was Sakra, her beloved husband. He did what was best in any given situation.

Indrani was living incognito, in a deep forest as a Sannyasin, a sage. She had left behind all pretentions of having been a former queen or the wife of one of the most powerful beings in the universe. She still was the child of Mahadeva in the depth of her hearts. Her routine prayer to Lord Shiva continued as devoutly as ever. Little did she know that she would be the trigger in the events that would reverse the domination of the Asuras and restore the Devas to their former glory.

As usual, she was plucking flowers in the jungle near her ashram, close to the river, completely unaware that Ajamukhi had put a huge price on her. Ajamukhi had not only promised riches and gold but also posts that rivalled the Asuras, under her brothers for those who gave her information about the whereabouts of Indrani and helped her to get her.

Every single enslaved being of the Asura empire and the menial Asuras themselves were hunting for Indrani. All they knew was that her beauty and her character were incomparable; she never blinked, worshipped Shiva diligently and would most likely be hiding as a sage devoted to Shiva, something she would not change. A sure giveaway was a common female sage who was very beautiful, never blinked and worshipped Shiva.

All Shiva temples were watched day in and out for anyone matching the above description. Indrani was the ticket to greatness. Ajamukhi also ordered that if anyone touched Indrani or informed her brothers, they would pay dearly. She personally wanted to take Indrani first to the one who had jilted her and break him.

Indrani proceeded to the river as was her routine, unaware that she was being watched by one of her own, a Deva who had escaped the Asura onslaught and now sought to return to his old normal life. The Deva did not care who he was under; all that mattered to him was his redemption and return to normalcy. He did not want to hide any longer. He was tired of being afraid. As soon as he heard the news that Indrani was viciously being hunted for, he knew whom to look for. He had seen her as his queen and now as a Sannyasin except that her face was as stoic as ever.

He quietly followed her without alarming her, watching from a safe distance.

Indrani went to the riverbank. She submerged herself in the water, came out without getting wet by virtue of her divinity because of her unflinching unquestioned devotion to her husband Indra. She then proceeded to sit under the Vilva tree (*Aegle Marmelos*), auspicious to Shiva, and took a handful of wet mud and moulded a linga, an iconic form of Lord Shiva. She then started chanting Rudram in her heart, losing herself in utter devotion.

This was the moment, thought the Deva. He knew that she would not move for some time, giving him the opportunity to reach Ajamukhi. He ran as fast as he could towards the Asura fort to send a message saying that he had important information for the Asura princess. The message was relayed quickly, albeit by an Asura captain who now imprisoned the Deva after finding out where Indrani was from him. Ajamukhi came in person, using the knowledge given to her by her mother Maya.

As soon as the Asura princess arrived, the captain told her all he knew from the Deva and said that he would take her to the location, assuring the princess that Indrani would still be there, praying to Lord Shiva. The captain obviously wanted to claim the reward for himself.

Ajamukhi and the Asura captain left with Ajamukhi's feared bodyguard to bring Indrani to Veeramahendrapuri and make an example of her. Indrani was still in deep meditation chanting Rudram when they arrived. Upon seeing her in person, Ajamukhi could not wait and pulled Indrani from her meditative posture and started dragging her by her hair.

As Indrani's chant was interrupted, a gruesome fearful figure with a giant sword appeared from the linga that she had built. 'Let her go this instant or lose your hand!' threatened the figure. The Asura princess defiantly stood her ground, 'How dare you talk to me like that! Do you know who I am?'

'I do not care who you are or who she is. Anyone who is devoted to Mahadeva, while chanting Rudram with single-minded devotion and absolute concentration, is under his protection. I will punish any person who dares touches them with maleficent intentions,' replied the figure.

'Finish him!' ordered the Asura princess, as both her bodyguard and the captain rushed towards the figure. In a single strike, the figure beheaded both, sending their heads rolling into the river as their lifeless bodies fell to the ground. Their bodies twitched for some time, unable to come to terms with the fact that they no longer had a head or that they were dead.

Ajamukhi was shocked! She had never seen an Asura beaten as if he did not matter. Her most fearsome bodyguard, who was her favourite lover, was no more. The captain of the fort was gone as well.

'If my brothers knew,' the enraged Ajamukhi started, but the figure cut her hand off in a single sweep, the same hand that held Indrani's hair. Blood spurting from what was left of her hand, Ajamukhi fell to the ground in shock. Indrani opened her eyes and prayed to the figure, which instructed her to continue her prayer and assured her that no harm will come to her, being a staunch devotee of Mahadeva.

Ajamukhi started to flee, but the figure did not seem to care. It disappeared into the linga as Indrani returned to her meditative posture and started chanting Rudram all over again. Ajamukhi was in pain, something she had never experienced before. She felt fear for the first time in her existence. She was without a limb, something she thought was impossible. She ran towards the fort in confusion, dazed. She fainted on the way, unable to run further.

When she woke up, she did not know how long she had been there. It felt like a nightmare until she realized that it wasn't a dream and she was still missing her arm. The linga was there but Indrani was not. The lifeless bodies of the Asuras were still lying there. She went back to her brother's palace in Veeramahendrapuri, using the mantras given by her mother. As she ran into the courtroom, her brothers were seated on their thrones.

Wrath

At the sight of their beloved little sister running in with loose hair, bloodied face and missing hand, the three brothers jumped up from their thrones and ran towards her. They caught her as she fell to the floor.

'What happened, Aja?! Who did this to you? Who dared touch our beloved sister, the Asura princess, Ajamukhi? Have they been slain already?' raged Sura.

Tarakasura immediately took out his giant sword and

summoned all the guards. 'Who knows how this happened? Tell me now or lose your life! Where is her bodyguard? Look for him immediately!' he thundered.

Simhamukha carried his sister to the throne and laid her down gently. He wiped her face clean and gave her some water to drink, while Sura summoned the Ashwins, the divine doctors.

They came and treated her with herbs, and said that she needed rest. However, they looked down and were unable to answer when asked if she would get her hand back. They did not have either the heart or the courage to tell the Asuras, both as brothers who loved their sister to death and as fearsome emperors, that their sister's hand was gone forever. Sura dismissed them.

He summoned his minister who also led the spies to find out what happened. 'Brother,' he heard his sister call him in a feeble voice at that instant. He turned and ran towards her, as did Tarakasura.

'What happened, my child? Who did this to you?' asked the brothers.

'Indrani did this to me. I went to capture her as a gift for you, my brother,' she said, looking at Sura.

'You should have called me! You are still a child. What happened to your bodyguard? Did he desert you?' asked the emperor.

'She killed him too,' responded Ajamukhi.

Sura turned to his minister. 'I want the one who did this to my sister in front of me in chains. Torture any Deva you can find and extract information about the whereabouts of Indrani. I will personally destroy her!' thundered Sura.

'Wait, brother!' said Simhamukha. Sura turned slowly towards him. This was the first time that he was hearing an opinion contrary to his and it was from his own brother. He nodded at him to go on.

'We have been ruling for centuries. The Devas have been subdued and have been our slaves for the entire time. Our sister too had her free reign with any and every creature she wanted. No trouble came to us till now. What changed? What wrong could our sister have done to warrant this situation? The person who lost her hand is no ordinary Asuri. She is the daughter of Kashyapa and Surasai. She is well versed in Maya. She is also unconditionally backed by the three of us. If her hand has been cut off and her fierce bodyguard has been killed, we should find out more about what really happened before taking any action. It could be our sister's mistake too. What if she had forgotten that it is the three of us who got boons from Shiva and imitated us, incurring the wrath of a mighty enemy? Do you believe Indrani is really capable of killing her bodyguard, let alone cutting off Ajamukhi's hand?' wondered Simhamukha.

Sura was silent.

'Brother!' cried Ajamukhi. 'Are you afraid? How can you call yourself an Asura? You are praising an enemy who has stood up and challenged the might of the Asuras!'

'If I may speak, O supreme ruler,' interjected the Asura's minister Amoghan. He was a learned Asura who had been trained directly by Sukhra for centuries. He was held in high esteem by all three Asura brothers.

'Proceed,' commanded Sura.

'I agree with what Simhamukha said. We should not take this lightly and react emotionally. We have been unchallenged thus far in the multiverse. No one stood up to the Asuras, let alone fight us. Ajamukhi's bodyguard is the first Asura that did not die a natural death for over three centuries. She is the first Asuri who was maimed since your highness won the great war. There is more to the incident than meets the eye and it needs thorough investigation, in my humble opinion, your highness,' said Amoghan.

Sura's eyes turned towards Ajamukhi. She started to wail. All the wise words that reached Sura's ears were blocked by sight of his beloved sister's tears.

'I have listened to your counsel. Now, as your emperor, do

as I order. Torture every single Deva you can find, till you find Indrani. Every single Deva will pay for what an Asuri had to endure. Once you find her, bind her and bring her to me,' Sura instructed and left the room.

Amoghan left the room, as did Simhamukha. Tarakasura sat with his sister as she dozed off to sleep.

Indra

*I*ndra came out of hiding frothing at his mouth in rage upon hearing about the assault on his wife. He had been hiding. He likened it to a tiger staying hidden for the right opportunity to pounce. He needed to be alive, active and ready to fight when the time came, but the assault on his wife was something he could not let pass. It was true that he had abandoned the women and children when he was supposed to escort them to safety. It was true that he had abandoned his wife. If he was caught, everything would be over, so he disguised himself and reached the gates of Satyaloka. Brahma, Narada and Brihaspati were there, engaged in a debate. Indra was irate.

'My wife has just been assaulted! You three are sitting here wasting time on a debate on some useless stuff, instead of seeing what can be done to bring down the Asuras!' shouted Indra.

'Indra! Remember who you are talking to,' Brahma stood up in rage at the insult. Indra shivered in fear at the sight of Brahma in anger. Brihaspati and Narada calmed both of them and seated them. Narada informed Indra that Indrani was now safe in Kailash.

'You abandoned not only your wife and the women who you were supposed to protect, but also all the Devas who relied on you for guidance and leadership. You stayed hidden for centuries. You have the audacity to question us, who stood firm here and faced the Asuras and their ill-treatment?' asked Brahma.

'I apologize, Grandsire. I was beside myself. Please forgive me,' pleaded Indra as he prostrated before Brahma.

'You cannot defeat Surapadma. Only Shiva's power can defeat him. Shiva however is engaged in deep meditational discourses with the Kumaras. Even if he were to wake up, he himself won't touch Surapadma and his brothers, for they are his staunch devotees who diligently worship him day in and day out,' replied Brahma.

'Are we to endure the Asuras for eternity then, Grandsire?' asked Indra. 'Was attending Daksha's yagna such a big crime?'

'Yes, it was a big crime,' replied Brahma. 'Shakti has now reincarnated as Parvati, daughter of Himavat. She is in deep penance, worshipping Shiva to marry him. If Shiva were to wake up, he surely would go to her and set things in motion for him to have an offspring who would take care of Surapadma.'

'Thank you, Grandsire, for showing me the way. I will follow your advice,' replied Indra.

'Wait, Indra,' Narada said. 'Tell us what you are thinking. We cannot afford any more mistakes.'

Kamadeva

'No!' cried Kama emphatically. It was a word Indra was not used to hearing from any Deva. Blood rushed to his head as soon as he heard the word.

'How dare you speak to me like that!' Indra advanced on Kama, but Narada stopped him.

'Get a hold of yourself, Indra. You are no longer the king of the Devas, let alone the universe. You need his help, he does not need yours,' said the travelling sage.

'Narada Muni, do you agree with this plan? Waking up Shiva

from his meditation is inviting certain death, even if you have had all the Amrut in the universe. He is capable of putting an end to any creation within the frame of time and space. He is Mahakaal! It is not merely about my existence. Imagine what would happen if he were to find out about this fiendish plan of Indra and your support for it. Do you honestly believe that you will be able to take his wrath? Besides, there is no guarantee that my Kamabana will work on Mahadeva. I will bet my life against it, as I am more inclined to believe that it will not work on him. All this exercise will be for nought. I am willing to give my life for the betterment of the Devas, but not when I know that it would be a sacrifice that does not affect the condition or well-being of the Devas one iota,' pleaded Kama.

'Even if my husband agrees, I will not allow him to partake in this activity, O vile Indra!' said Rati, face growing red in anger while tears rolled down her cheeks in fear of her husband's life. Rati had no reason to fear or respect Indra. She had seen Indra cower before her father, Daksha, before the yagna. She always saw him more as an opportunistic fox than a valiant Deva.

'Calm down, my dear children!' replied Narada. 'This is a mere option we are discussing. No one can or has any power now to force you to do anything other than Sura or his brothers. You have no obligation to obey me or Indra now. We wanted to know your opinion on the idea and, more importantly, if it would work. Indra will take the blame if things go out of hand. You will not come to any harm in any of the outcomes,' concluded Narada.

'But,' hesitated Kama and Rati interjected, 'How can you trust Indra to come and own up to his mistakes? Are you talking about the same Indra who ran away at the sight of Veerabhadra, without even standing up for a second, and clearing the way for him to reach my father? Are you talking about the same Indra who did not pay any respect to my father, his own grandfather, for centuries once he lost his head as well as his position as the ruler of the universe? Are you talking about the same Indra who did nothing to stop the Asuras when he knew very well that any Asura doing penance for Mahadeva is bound to come after him? Are you talking about the same Indra who deserted the battlefield, leaving his own son, his beloved prince, to face the mighty Asuras while running away with the women and children as one of them in pretext of protecting them while Jayanta, Jwala and Agni fought valiantly and Yama faced the Asura brothers? Are you talking about the same Indra who deserted the women and children upon hearing the victory conch of the Asuras and ran away leaving behind even his Vajrayudha? He not only deserted the women and children but also his own wife and son when the mighty Asura's onslaught began. Are you telling me, Maharishi, that the same Indra would come forward to sacrifice himself and save my husband from certain death were we to incur the wrath of Mahadeva?'

Indra could not control his anger any more. What made him even angrier was the fact that every word his aunt, the wretched daughter of Daksha, spoke, was the truth. That was how every single being, including his family, his clan and the Devas, and even his enemy the Asuras, saw him. He held himself back, considering that his anger, if directed towards Rati or Kama, would affect him more than it would affect them.

Narada was quiet for a moment and then said, 'If Indra is your problem, my children, then let me assure you that the plan is not Indra's but my father, Brahma's. Vishnu suggested that the child of Mahadeva alone can destroy the Asuras. Brahma suggested that unless we wake up Mahadeva and get him to marry Parvati, there was no redemption for the ones oppressed by the Asuras.'

'Let us go to Brahma then. I will plead my case to him directly,' replied Rati before Kama could say another word. He realized that he did not have the mental strength to say no to Indra or Narada. Neither could he face Rati if he agreed to their demands.

It was better for him to leave the decision to her, rather than to himself or Indra.

Rati

'*G*randsire!' called Rati as soon as she saw Brahma. He welcomed her with open arms and she fell to his feet, as did Kamadeva.

'Sukhi Bhava!' granted Brahma. It meant 'stay happy' as opposed to his usual 'Ayushman Bhava' which meant 'live a long and healthy life'. They both got up. Rati was in tears.

'So, you too are a part of this, as Narada said,' said Rati as she wiped her tears.

Rati was one of the daughters of Daksha and the sister of Aditi, the mother of the Devas. Daksha was the favourite son, also called Prajapati, meaning leader of the populace. He held the high seat for eons, before his position got to his head, leading him to lose the same. After losing his head and getting the head of a goat, he went to a forest, relinquishing all his belongings, to pray to Mahadeva and repent his actions. That was when Indra climbed to the top over his stepbrothers the Asuras, clearly being the favourite over the much weaker Atisuran, the then ruler of the Asuras.

'Yes, my child. I know how difficult this is for you and Kama. But, if there was any other choice, I would have gone for it. You are my children, you all are. Sometimes, for the greater good, we need to take risks. If someone else could have done it, I would not have approved Indra seeking Kama's help,' explained Brahma.

'Why should I sacrifice my life for someone who deserted me and my race at the first sign of trouble? More than death, the thought of parting with my Rati scares me, O Grandfather!' said Kama.

'Would Indra sacrifice himself for the greater good in a similar situation, Grandsire?' asked Rati. The rage in her eyes would have burnt Indra, had she had the power. Indra could feel it in himself and he had no answer. He was grateful that the question went to Brahma and not to him.

'As your grandsire, Kama and Rati, I request you, beseech you, to try and unite Shiva and Parvati so that we all can go back to how things were,' Brahma pleaded.

'Everyone will go back to how things were, Grandsire. What about me? What about my beloved Kama?' asked Rati angrily, enraging Brahma.

'If both of you are not willing to listen to your Grandsire Brahma, then you will have to deal with Brahma the creator, the progenitor among the Trimurtis,' he said as he stood up. He towered like a giant, holding a bow and his dreaded Brahmastra, which had the power to destroy anything it was aimed at, provided that it was created by Brahma directly or indirectly. That included more or less all life forms in all the multiverses, barring Mahadeva, Vishnu and their consorts.

Kama shuddered at the sight of the mighty Brahma standing before him, and so did Rati, Indra and Narada. They had never seen their progenitor as a warrior. They merely saw him as a wise counsel and a gentle senior who guided them when they needed it the most. This form of Brahma was new to all of them.

'Please sire, I apologize for letting my tongue lose. Please spare me and please spare my husband,' implored Rati.

'If the fear of the life of your husband is your only concern, Rati, then your husband's fate is sealed. He either faces my wrath or that of Mahadeva's,' thundered Brahma.

'But think about...' started Rati as Kama interjected, 'I will go, Grandsire,' in a calm voice. Indra smiled, after a long time.

'I would like to speak to my wife in private for a moment,' said Kama as he took his wife aside.

'I would rather die at the hands of Mahadeva himself and

get Moksha than die at the hands of Brahma and continue the cycle of birth as anyone but your husband. Mahadeva is also the kindest and most selfless. He is more likely to forgive me and is more capable of restoring me than Brahma. I am doing this to protect us, Rati. Trust me,' said Kama.

'I love you. I will plead to Mahadeva and Parvati. I will somehow get you back,' promised Rati and they embraced.

'Let us go,' said Kama as he took out his sugarcane bow and five-flowered arrow, and they all ventured towards Kailash.

Nandi

'Who goes there?' asked Nandi upon hearing footsteps. He was fully armed and ready for a face-off as soon as he heard footsteps. He inferred that it was a group and not a peaceful one, as rishis wore no footwear. Considering that the current rulers were Asuras, Nandi was more or less on his toes, expecting the Asuras to turn their backs on their benefactors as they mostly had done at one time or other.

Nandi had been born to the sage Shilada, whose sole ambition had been to beget an immortal son, who would be the greatest devotee as well as the prime servant of Mahadeva himself. From the fire of a yagna performed by Shilada, rose a form with the head of a bull and an impregnable body made of a glittering diamond-like substance. In addition to becoming the prime servant, gatekeeper, mount and most ardent devotee of Mahadeva, Nandi also became, by the grace of the lord, the prime disciple of Mahadeva, who taught him everything, ranging from yoga to dance, to playing Miruthangam (Indian drum), to tantric rituals as well as warfare.

Nandi's devotion to Mahadeva was so great that when the latter was pleased with Nandi as a student and asked him to ask for a boon, Nandi merely asked that no one should be allowed into Kailash unless they were allowed in by Nandi, after taking permission from Mahadeva. This boon meant that if Nandi did not allow someone when Mahadeva had instructed him not to, nothing in the universe could defeat or beat Nandi and enter the abode of the supreme lord. This was pretty much common knowledge across the universes.

'It is I, Brahma, the progenitor among Trimurtis and the grandsire of all beings, including thyself, Nandi. I am here along with Indra, Narada, Kama and Rati to see Mahadeva,' responded Brahma.

'With all due respect, Sir, you are not my grandsire, for you have not created me. I was not born from my father and mother, but came from a yagna conducted according to the instructions of Mahadeva himself. My father, though, can call you grandsire. Being the progenitor among Trimurtis, I bow to thee.

'As far as seeing Mahadeva goes, I have specific instructions not to let anyone inside,' said Nandi, being both a symbol of humility as well as insurmountable power when he was in Kailash.

Brahma, being wise, knew that there was no force that could defeat Nandi when he was on guard in Kailash. Indra, the unwise, let his arrogance speak.

'The nerve of you bull-headed moron, to not only stop one of the Trimurtis but the king of the Devas!' said Indra, feeling insulted at being stopped by a half-man, half-bull centaur.

'Indra!' thundered Nandi, enraged at the insult. He grew in size in his anger, ready for a full-fledged armed confrontation. 'Do not forget who you are and what your position is! You are now but a mere fugitive who has forsaken his honour and morals. Your selfishness alone has brought this wretched fate on the Devas. You aimed to please Daksha so that he would pick you as his heir apparent, which led to your present situation. I swear in the name of the supreme lord, one more word of arrogance, and I will make your condition so much worse that you will regret not being captured by the Asuras. Do not push your luck!'

Indra cowered at the sight of the gigantic, war-ready Nandi. Narada intervened, making peace.

'Nandideva, kindly forgive his ignorance and arrogance. Brahma and I are not here merely for him, but for the well-being of the multiverse. It is not merely the Devas who are being punished. Indrani, the queen mother of the Devas, was attacked by Ajamukhi while she was engaged in worship of Mahadeva himself. She was saved at the last moment by Mahadeva's grace. The Asuras no longer respect the lord. Besides, the objective of Kama being here is to put an end to Mahadeva's solitude and inaction by reuniting him with the holy mother Shakti, who has reincarnated as Parvati,' explained Narada.

'That is good news. Nothing would please me more than the sight of my lord being happy and in marital bliss. However, I have been given specific instructions and I will not allow anyone inside contrary to that,' replied Nandi.

'What do we do now, Nandideva? Neither are you giving us access nor are you directing us how to get the same,' said Narada.

'Go to the one you always go to at times of trouble,' clued in Nandi. While Indra looked at Brahma, Narada understood what Nandi meant.

They all went to Vaikunta. Narayana sat up from his slumber. Without saying a word, he took off his necklace and placed it around the neck of Kama. The rest of the group started to leave while Rati fell at Narayana's feet.

Paramatma understood what she wanted and said to her, 'All this is already done. I will take care of this. You will reunite with your husband physically once again when I take the avatar of Krishna. He will be born as my son and you will be his wife.'

Nandi, upon seeing the necklace around Kama's neck, allowed all of them enter. He bowed respectfully to Narada and Brahma.

He patted Kama on the back, understanding what the ultimate outcome of their misadventure would be. Kama and Rati threw themselves at his feet. 'May success be yours for the sake of Kailash, if not the universe,' blessed Nandi.

When Indra crossed Nandi, he merely stared deep into his being. Indra avoided eye contact from fear and shame. Nandideva stopped him, looked him up and down with scorn and then let him pass. The only way to win respect and grace from Nandideva was to be an ardent devotee of or, at the very least, be highly respectful of the supreme lord Mahadeva. Indra, like Daksha, was lacking on that front.

Ananga

The group entered the pristine abode of the lord. It was as beautiful as ever.

Kama stood behind a Vilva tree in the cave, hoping to protect himself from the wrath of Mahadeva for what he was going to do or rather was being forced to do. Brahma, Indra, Narada and Rati stood outside the cavern where Mahadeva was instructing the Kumaras.

Kama sought the blessings of his father Brahma and Mahavishnu. He then sought penance from Mahadeva, before taking out his bow. It was a beautiful bow made from a fully grown, fresh, ripe sugarcane. He proceeded to take an arrow made by attaching five flowers, Aravinda, Ashoka, Choota, Navamallika, and Neelotpala, whose combined fragrance resulted in an instant awakening of romantic feelings. As soon as the fragrance of the flowers spread, the Vilva tree blossomed. Bees, cuckoos and parrots flocked towards Kailash, which was otherwise clad in snow and had nothing to offer to any of them.

Kama then released the arrow after chanting the Mohanastotram. It arrow flew past Rati, Indra, Brahma, Narada and Nandi, towards Mount Meru. It touched Parvati and in that instant, all her absolute devotion towards Mahadeva turned into love for him. Flowers blossomed all around Mount Meru.

Kama took a second arrow, repeated the same procedure and shot it towards Mahadeva. The arrow flew past the Kumaras and touched Mahadeva's body. Kailash shook for a second. Brahma and Indra were ecstatic, thinking that it had worked.

Except that it did not. Mahadeva, who was in the deepest meditation possible, was more disturbed and angry than aroused. In his wrath, he opened his eyes. Unfortunately for Kama, Mahadeva's third eye opened along with his other two and cosmic flames burst out, melting the snow on the mountains.

Brahma sweated profusely. Indra and Narada fainted, unable to bear the heat. Nandi shuddered. Rati started wailing and fainted as the fire moved straight towards the Vilva tree. The tree and Kama, hiding behind the tree, were burnt down to ashes. Mahadeva closed his third eye immediately but it was too late: Kama was no more.

Rati regained consciousness and rushed towards the ashes, but they were still smouldering and burnt her hands. She ran to Mahadeva and hugged his feet.

'O lord of the gods! O supreme godhead! O peerless one! What did we do to deserve this punishment? All this was done thanks to Brahma, who threatened my husband with dire consequences if he refused. We did this to unite you and Parvati, so that the son born to you can put an end to the Asuras and free the Devas.

'Why did you not direct your wrath at the arrow instead of the person who shot it? Your grace and kindness is unparalleled, Mahadeva! Kindly redeem and give me back my husband. Please forgive him or open your third eye and burn me to ashes. If I cannot live with my husband as a person, I will merge my ashes with his. If I can't share his life, let me share his fate,' implored

Rati, crying her heart out at the death of her husband.

'My child,' said the lord, 'there is no need for you to cry. I can and will give back the soul of your husband, for it belongs to me and has reached me. He will, however, not be able to retain his physical form, for what has been incinerated by the cosmic fire cannot be restored. He will be formless, Ananga, to the rest of us. For you, he will be able to manifest as a soul and join you. As Mahavishnu blessed you, you two will physically unite in Dwapara Yuga.'

He then turned and summoned Brahma and Indra. They told him what he already knew, that the Asuras were torturing the Devas, that they had gone after one of his most ardent devotees, Indrani, and that Parvati was waiting to become his consort.

Shiva smilingly said, 'Do not worry, O wise one. I will go to Parvati, test her devotion and love and make her my consort right away.' He then turned to the Kumaras, who prostrated themselves before him, blessed them, asked them to go to Nandi, to continue their instruction.

Parvati

*P*arvati did not know what had hit her and why she felt a certain way. She had followed her daily ritual, taken a bath, collected flowers to worship the lord and arka twigs (calatropis procera) for the yagna and gone back to her hut in the yagnashala, where she sat and chanted Rudram for the rest of the day, building a fire with the twigs she had collected. She had eaten only once that day before sunset, and the rest of her time had been devoted to prayer. She slept early and woke up before sunrise to start her ritual. She no longer draped herself in royal clothing and dressed as a Sannyasin. This was her usual routine, but this day turned out to be out of the ordinary.

Everything around her looked different and a lot more beautiful than before. Everything around her paired up: the swimming swans, the golden deer, cuckoos, parrots, peacocks, butterflies and bees dancing around her. The fully blossomed lotus, rose, tulips, lavender, chrysanthemum, lilac, jasmine, daffodils and screw-pine filled the air surrounding the mountains with fragrance. The whole atmosphere around her oozed of love. She felt like a grown woman yearning for the company of her one true love for the first time in her life, instead of a child adamantly devoted to god, seeking his lotus feet. Parvati was, after all, the gentler aspect of Shakti.

Parvati pulled herself together and walked briskly towards the hut without the flowers. She was stopped by an old man. He had a great white beard and looked like he was over a hundred years of age, his skin falling from his bones. He was draped in saffron, the traditional attire of those who have renounced the world. He had Vibhuti, sacred ash, smeared on his forehead and all over his body.

'May you get your heart's true desire, my child,' blessed the old man. 'Aren't you too young to become a Sannyasin? You will fall in love, want to get married, have children. All those desires are yet to well up inside you. Once they arrive, devotion disappears. Once you are done with those emotions and then become a Sannyasin, it will be permanent,' said the old man.

'Nothing is permanent, O seer. Nothing except Sadasiva is permanent,' said Parvati humbly.

'Shakti is permanent. Shiva derives all his power and energy from Shakti. Shiva without Shakti is but a mere corpse,' said the old sage to test her.

'Sadasiva and Shakti are one and the same. They are not separate from each other, nor are they separable. My lord, Mahadeva, who is Sadasiva's incarnate in the current epoch, may be without Shakti now, but I will join him and become his Shakti,' said Parvati.

'You speak as if you do not seek a place at his feet but in his heart, my child,' said the old man.

'I seek to be his. That is all I seek,' replied Parvati. The old man blessed her and went away.

At the entrance to her hut stood a handsome young man. His skin glittered, and his facial features were sharp. He was muscular and well-built, with long curly golden hair. His blue eyes shone; his lips were full and red. He had a perfect set of well-lined, white teeth.

Parvati bowed to him and asked, 'Are you a traveller? You must have come here by mistake. This is a Sannyasin's hut.' She tried to enter her hut as she spoke and the handsome man stopped her, expecting her to lose her temper.

However, she smiled at him and said, 'My son, there is nothing for you here, like I said before. If you want, you can take some rest after eating the fruits, and then leave.'

'You must be blind. No woman who has seen me has called me her son. You are not even half my age and you see me as your son?' asked the shocked young man.

'I am going to be his wife, the supreme lord's wife. Everything that ever was, is and will be, came from him. If he is the father of all that is created, then I, by virtue of being his Shakti, will be the mother. I am your mother as well, my child,' said Parvati.

'Have you seen him? His hair is dirty and matted. He smears ashes from corpses all over his body. He wears tigerskin for clothing. He adorns his neck with a live snake. He resides in the cold Kailash. His favourite hunting ground for food is a cremation ground. You are such a beautiful young girl with a vibrant aura. Your eyes show the depth of love. Your form is divine. You deserve someone who is full of life. Heed me. I will marry you. I am a Gandharva prince. We will live a full life, have the most handsome children and rule my kingdom is bliss,' the man pleaded.

'My son, neither do I seek pleasures of the skin, nor do I seek riches. My life is full. My life becomes full whenever I chant the name of my lord. He may be as you described, but without him, we will cease to exist. Your hair will fall off, your skin will wrinkle and your body will become bent, but he is eternal. He does not change. Do not talk badly of my husband, Shiva, for I will not forgive you twice,' said Parvati, entering her hut.

Parvati was a little confused by the two encounters of the day. She called Jaya and Vijaya, but they were nowhere to be found. Meru was usually quiet, with no other being in the vicinity, except birds and animals. Yet, she had met two men on the same day.

'My dear Parvati!' called a voice from outside the hut. She lost her temper at the address and came out angrily, but she was pleasantly shocked. In front of her, both the old seer and Gandharva prince stood, and they merged into one and became her lord, Shiva. Tears rolled down her cheeks as she fell to his feet. He lifted her up.

'Go to your parents. I will come and seek your hand. Our marriage will happen soon,' blessed the lord as he disappeared. Parvati rushed to her parents' abode.

Mainavati

'We are indeed blessed to have Brahma, Indra, Narada and Mahavishnu visit our humble abode,' said Himavat, who for all intents and purposes was a small king in the Himalayan range, far off and safe from both Deva and Asura reach, with nothing to offer to either.

'Kindly accept our salutations and humble welcome,' said Himavat and Mainavati in unison as they prostrated before their honoured guests. 'Our daughter, Parvati, just informed us that she was visited by Parameswara himself, who had sought her hand in marriage. We cannot say no to her, for she is not our daughter born of us. We merely brought her up. We found her inside a lotus in Mana Sarovar Lake. She had three eyes and eight hands when we found her. She became as she is now once my wife, her adoptive mother, touched her. Parvati's decision is ours and we now know her decision as well as destiny is to become Shiva's wife. I would have no objection whatsoever to this union, even if I had a say. What about you, my queen?' asked Himavat.

'We are indeed blessed to have the great god Parameswara himself as our son-in-law, but...' trailed off Mainavati. Indra was shocked. Brahma and Narada were confused. Mahavishnu smiled.

'Do not worry, Mainavati. Your concerns are unfounded. However, feel free to express them. Marriages should be founded on truth and all involved must be wholeheartedly so. Being the mother of Parvati, you have all the right in the world to be concerned and express the same. Be open and share your thoughts fearlessly,' said Paramatma.

'Thank you, my lord. My concerns are two-fold. One, Parameswara was already married and is a widower. That is not a concern. My concern is what happened to his former father-in-law. Parameswara could not and did not get along with his father-in-law and the great Daksha Prajapati met with a cruel fate. I dread the same for my husband.

'My other concern is with the marriage. Last time, when the lord married Sati, he simply took her away. Parvati is our only daughter. We want her marriage to happen in a grand manner, inviting all the Devas, Asuras, Nagas, Gandharvas, rishis, Vasus. It is not merely to show off our wealth or for our pride but because we want this union to be blessed by one and all,' concluded Mainavati.

Indra grimaced at the mention of the Asuras. He did not have any choice in the matter, though. If the Asuras were indeed going to come, he would have to take a backseat.

Mahavishnu replied, 'Regarding your first concern, I will adopt

Parvati as my sister. I will conduct the ceremony as her guardian, taking her father's position. Therefore, the fate and destiny intended for the father-in-law of Parameswara will be mine. I will bear the brunt of whatever is to befall the bride's father.

'As far as your second concern, I will talk to the lord and make him accept your proposal of a grand marriage. I will make all the elaborate arrangements for the wedding from the bride's side as well, being her brother. This wedding will be attended by everyone in the multiverse. This will be the grandest wedding that has ever taken place and ever will take place. The first honour shall go to your husband, King Himavat. Does that alleviate your worries, Mother?' asked Mahavishnu.

'We are indeed fortunate and blessed,' replied Mainavati. 'Not only are we getting Parameswara as our son-in-law but Paramatma as our son. All this is due to the grace of the lord and us getting Parvati as our daughter.'

'Mother, not only are you getting Parameswara was your son-in-law and Paramatma as your son, but also you already have Parvati as your daughter. She is none other than the gentlest aspect of Shakti. Blessed are you two. She chose you as her parents because of your piety and devotion to Mahadeva,' said Vishnu.

Both Mainavati and Himavat prostrated themselves before Mahavishnu, tears rolling down their cheeks. Mahavishnu stopped them and said, 'It is I who should prostrate myself at your feet, being your son,' as he prostrated himself before them.

Seeing Mahavishnu do so, Brahma and the rest followed. The proud parents closed their eyes and thanked their daughter, Parvati, and future son-in-law, Mahadeva for all the grace, love, honour and respect they were receiving.

Nuptial

$\mathcal{T}$he venue of the marriage ceremony was shifted to Kailash to accommodate the huge guest list. It involved everyone who was anyone in all existence. Being a neutral venue and with no one wanting to incur the wrath of Mahadeva or Mahavishnu, enmities were forgotten for the time being. The Asura scion attended the ceremony along with his siblings and mother. He also allowed the Devas to attend the ceremony, barring the troublemakers. Agni, Vayu, Yama, Surya, Chandra and Indra were in attendance. Indra hoped to get a glimpse of Jayanta but unbeknownst to him, Jayanta was still in a catatonic state. Indra's blood boiled at the sight of Surapadma and the thought of his wife's attacker being respected at the event. Surapadma, however, did not care or turn his attention to Indra. This was not the place or the time. Further, he had guards ready at the foot of Kailash to catch Indra were he to come out alone even for a second. Surapadma's devotion to Mahadeva was still second to none and he respected him infinitely. He celebrated the wedding as a holy ceremony, and festivities were huge and endless in Veeramahendrapuri as well as in Asurapuri and Mayapuri. Simhamukha was filled with joy upon realizing that he was going to witness his divine mother, the one he worshipped every day, for the first time in her gentler aspect. From the rishis' side, everyone from Brihaspati to Sukhra was in attendance. Vasus, Gandharvas, Nagas, Asuras, Devas, Brahma, Vishnu, Narada and their families were present in one location, Kailash.

Brahma played the master of ceremonies. He chanted the wedding mantra as the ceremony commenced. The rishis repeated the mantra after him. Nandi was playing the Miruthangam while Saraswati played the Veena. Rambha, Menaka, Urvashi and Tilottama danced, thanks to the Sura brothers. The music echoed across the universe joyfully, as day-to-day troubles were forgotten.

It was a pious, holy, happy and harmonious environment with the best of music, food and entertainment. All were equal in front of Mahadeva's eyes and all were treated as such, irrespective of their race, position or clan. The wedding decorations and altar arrangements were done by Vishwakarma himself. Kubera, as ordered by Sura, spared no expense and gave everything he had to help the wedding.

Brahma asked for the groom to be invited to the altar. Since Vishnu was representing the bride's side, Brahma ushered in Mahadeva. The moment he entered, no one could take their eyes off the supreme lord: his appearance was a pleasant shock to everyone. They had never seen him like that before. When one mentions Mahadeva, all one can picture is someone wearing tigerskin and ashes. That day, he came clad in gold from head to toe. His clear face was marked by Vibhuti on the forehead in an arched pattern that flowed with his eyebrows. Mahavishnu, who was in charge of dressing the bridegroom, had done a splendid job. The form of the formless was not something one had ever seen or will ever get to see again in their existence.

Brahma ushered in the bridegroom and seated him at the altar in front of Agni, and chanted mantras invoking goodwill. Soon the time came for him to summon the bride. Mainavati, accompanied by Pativratas (women who were steadfast in their devotion to their husband by thought, word and action), brought Parvati to the altar, singing auspicious songs. Mahavishnu, who was waiting there, took the place of her guardian, held her hand and took her to the altar.

At that moment, Mahavishnu, Mahaprajapati and Mahadeva were in the same place, along with Mahashakti's incarnates Saraswati, Lakshmi and Parvati. Everyone in the wedding hall was filled with eternal bliss, truly blessed to bear witness to this beautiful sight.

Brahma solemnized the marriage, looking around to ensure that everyone was happy with the wedding. Mahadeva asked Brahma to wait for a moment. This sent a chill down Mainavati's spine, who still dreaded the thought of her husband becoming the father-in-law of Mahadeva and incurring the fate of Daksha. Mahadeva turned towards a far corner, where a Deva woman was silently crying. It was Rati.

Mahadeva lifted his right hand and Kamadeva's soul flew from his hand in the form of light and moved amidst the crowd towards Rati. She felt the light over her and the touch of her husband who had been burnt to ashes. Her tears of sorrow turned to tears of joy.

'Kama!' she cried. The light entered Rati and their two souls became one. She ran and fell at Mahadeva's feet, who blessed them. Mainavati was relieved.

As Brahma proceeded to solemnize the wedding, the whole altar, along with the mountain on which it was built, shook and sank down. The guests feared for their existence. Was it the time of Pralaya (end of the earth), they wondered.

Himavat ran to Mahadeva and asked, 'Why does this inauspicious event happen during a wedding, my lord?'

Mahadeva smiled and replied, 'Do not worry, Himavat. This is not an inauspicious event. When the three of us are together, there cannot be inauspiciousness. There is no inauspiciousness when achieving a good end through a good deed with good intentions. This is merely a physical imbalance caused by all of us being at the same place at the same time.'

'O lord! Do you then ask us to leave for our abodes without attending the wedding?' asked Indra.

'No, Sakra. It is enough if one among us goes off to the south to balance the rest of us crowding the north,' replied Mahadeva.

'Who will it be, my lord?' asked Indra.

'Agastya,' called out Mahadeva. Agastya was a rishi. He was also a dwarf and was always looked down upon both literally and figuratively by the rest of the Devas and rishis. He, however, was one of the staunchest devotees of Mahadeva. His devotion rivalled

Nandi's and, unlike Nandi, his devotion was by choice and not chance.

'Yes, Father,' answered Agastya. He had been born out of a pot and did not have a father or a mother. It was one another reason why he wasn't treated well. Neither did he originate through Brahma and nor was he as powerful as the Trimurti. He was an anomaly to everyone. He considered Mahadeva to be his father and believed that the reason for his existence was to serve, worship and pray to the lord.

'Go down south below the Vindhyas. Reside there. I will guide your actions,' said Mahadeva. Agastya started to cry inconsolably. Narada, one of the few who were his friends, as well as one of the few who treated him as an equal, ran to him and asked him what was wrong.

'I am an accursed creature. While the whole of the multiverse is going to bear witness to this holy union, I am to leave this place. What is my sin, O father!' enquired Agastya.

'No, Agastya. You are one of the most gifted of all beings. The role you are going to play will shape the future of the multiverse. If not being able to see my wedding is what bothers you, at any time you desire, close your eyes and think of me. I, along with my wife, Parvati, will appear before you as we were at the moment the wedding was solemnized,' replied Mahadeva.

Agastya fell to Mahadeva's feet and left. The balance, as Mahadeva had said, was restored. Brahma continued the rituals and solemnized the wedding. Mahavishnu held Parvati's hand and placed it over Mahadeva's, making them man and wife, while Brahma chanted the mantras and Saraswati poured holy water to solemnize the wedding. Mahalakshmi, taking the role of Mahadeva's sister, completed the rituals prescribed to be performed by the bridegroom's sister. As soon as Mahadeva's hand touched Parvati's, she knew who she was and what her destiny truly was.

The guests ate to their hearts' content and left. Indra and

Vayu quietly stayed back, for they knew what awaited them if they were to leave Kailash.

Durvasa

Hell hath no fury like a woman scorned. Double that for Ajamukhi, who had never heard the word 'no' or had any brush with failure. Within a short span of time, she met both and it was eating away inside her.

On the way back to Veeramahendrapuri, Ajamukhi wandered off. Her brothers, who were used to her behaviour, let her be, as it was safe territory, triangulated between Veeramahendrapuri on one side, Asurapuri on another and Mayapuri on the third. The sight of a wedding, something she knew that she would not ever experience out of free will of the groom, especially without an arm, agitated her and made her thirsty for love. All she now wanted was children. Unfortunately, a seer named Durvasa was passing through the forest. He was infamous for his wrath and the power of his curse. The moment Ajamukhi laid eyes upon Durvasa, all her hatred and thirst turned towards him.

'Stop! Be mine now!' she ordered.

'What! How dare you talk to me like that! Don't you know who I am? I am Durvasa. Leave now, before I curse you with a fate that is worse than death!' thundered Durvasa, enraged.

'Don't you dare refuse me, sage! I am Ajamukhi, sister of Surapadma, Tarakasura and Simhamukha. We rule the multiverse now. Your curse may hurt me, but what my brothers will do to you will hurt even more! You are in my land, surrounded by the empire of my brothers. Succumb to my desire now and give me an offspring. Else, you will regret the day you came into existence!' shrieked Ajamukhi.

Durvasa understood the situation, swallowed his pride for once in his life and yielded to her.

Out of this dalliance between a very angry, evil and impious Asuri and a very angry, wrathful, powerful, proud and hurt seer, twins were born. Ilvala and Vatapi were their names, Ilvala being the elder. Durvasa did not want to have anything to do with all three of them and left the place as quickly as possible.

Ajamukhi ordered Ilvala and Vatapi to do penance to Brahma and get boons that will render them powerful and immortal. She also ordered them to punish and hurt as many Shiva devotees as possible, especially rishis, as vengeance for their current situation. Evil by nature, they did as their mother ordered and started a severe penance to Brahma.

Ajamukhi then went to Veeramahendrapuri, where Brahma was conducting the morning prayer for Surapadma as his official priest. She knew better than to interrupt her brother during his prayer and waited for it to be over. Once done, she ran to her brother and said, 'O Brother, I had two sons who are performing penance to Brahma. Ask him to appear before them and grant boons.'

'No, my little sister, that is not how boons work. Boons given and received under threat seldom work. The giver of the boon should give it wholeheartedly and the receiver should receive it wholeheartedly as well. If we could order boons, don't you think we would have got everything conceivable from Brahma, who is now my priest?' questioned Sura gently. Ajamukhi's face fell and she left. She let her sons continue their long and hard penance.

Suddenly, like a bolt out of the blue, she remembered that her mother had told her that Mahadeva had appeared to her brothers only after they sacrificed their lives, even though they had performed centuries of penance and yagna. She ran to her sons and instructed them to sacrifice their lives to Brahma.

Ilvala called his brother Vatapi, and asked him to submit to be sacrificed. Vatapi complied, so Ilvala invoked Brahma and cut his brother's head off. Brahma appeared immediately, equally from the fear of Sura's wrath if he were to know that Brahma had let his nephews die, and the sincerity in their penance, which made them ready to sacrifice their lives to please him.

'Call your brother's name, Ilvala, and he will come to life. For so long as you live, irrespective of which state he is in, your brother's life and form will be restored,' blessed Brahma, before quickly disappearing.

The brothers ran to their mother, who was pleased. She asked them to use the boon and kill as many Devas and rishis as possible. She also tutored them in the art of Maya and set them on course for their mission: to punish as many divine beings as possible. Unbeknownst to them, Durvasa, using all the power that he had gained through his penance, cursed that the three kingdoms that had trapped him in the land will be laid to waste when their rulers die.

Indra

'How much longer do we stay hidden here?' lamented Indra to Vayu. 'Wake Mahadeva up, they said. I sacrificed Kamadeva and did it. Get him married, they said, so I pushed Mahavishnu, Mahadeva and Brahma to get that done as well. I am not sure what more I should do for Mahadeva and Parvati to beget a son who would destroy the Asura and restore my position to me,' Indra continued peevishly.

At that very moment, a Gana (soldier of Mahadeva) came in.

'Indradeva, there is a messenger for you. He looks and smells like a Deva. Would you like to meet him?' asked the Gana.

'Yes. Please ask him to wait. I will come out and meet him,' replied Indra. He stepped out and the sight of the messenger filled him with joy.

'Tell me, tell me some good news. I could use some good news now,' said Indra to the messenger as he hugged him in excitement.

'Lord, I am afraid I do not have good news,' said the messenger, describing the events that led to the demoralization of Jayanta and finally his current catatonic state.

Indra rose in anguish and ran towards the abode of the supreme lord. He was in for more disappointment. He was shocked to see Mahadeva engaged in meditation again, while Parvati was busy worshiping him with flowers. But, after being a witness to what had happened to Kama, Indra dared not disturb him. He left quietly. Then, he ran to Vayu, picked him up and ran to Brahma.

'Grandsire, all my efforts have been in vain. Kama's sacrifice has been in vain. Mahadeva is back in his meditative trance and Parvati is again merely worshiping him. I have been let down,' said Indra.

Brahma smiled, hearing the words 'I', 'me' from the mouth of Indra. Narada arrived too. 'Well then, you need to find a way to wake up Mahadeva again and instead of using guile, plead with him to put an end to your misery,' replied Brahma. Narada almost laughed at the sarcasm but held back, considering the situation.

Indra quickly tuned to Vayu and said, 'My friend, my brother, I need you to help me.'

'No, not happening. Everyone knows the price a person must pay, who wakes up Mahadeva when he is in deep meditation. If you want to wake Mahadeva up, do it yourself. I would rather spend eternity as Sura's sweeper than incur Mahadeva's wrath,' said Vayu, backing off.

Indra pleaded with Agni and Yama as well, but his usual arrogance and fear of attaining the same fate as Kamadeva turned them away. Agni, however, was receptive to Brahma's idea of pleading to Mahadeva, for Mahadeva was kindness personified. Further, mother Parvati too was with him now and she would also insist that her husband help them.

Without someone to do the deed and without the courage to do it himself, Indra gathered Agni, Vayu, Brahma and Narada again to go to Mahadeva. Nandi, this time, allowed them in as Narada cleverly said that they were going to meet the holy mother and Nandi did not have any instruction from Mahadeva regarding allowing or disallowing people from meeting her.

Parvati was offended at being disturbed during her prayer, but upon seeing them accompanied by Brahma, she calmed down. Brahma asked Indra to narrate his case in detail. Parvati was the universal mother and upon hearing what had happened with Indrani and Jayanta, she lost her temper.

'I will wake him up,' said Parvati, who still hadn't realized her potential as the manifestation of Shakti. When asked, Mahadeva had told her that it was for Shakti to decide, not him.

'My lord,' called Parvati. Shiva was unmoved.

Kumarasambhava

Kumarasambhava

*I*ndra became apprehensive as the temperature in Kailash started to soar. Everyone's eyes started to burn and they began sweating profusely. Their bodies started shivering and an unknown, inexplicable fear engulfed them. The hair on their bodies stood up.

Mahadeva's body seemed to grow bigger and bigger by the minute. Mahavishnu came rushing in, not wanting to miss the spectacle, as did Nandi. The Ganas and the other inhabitants of Kailash started to run away in fear. The whole multiverse felt a strange vibration that struck fear in the hearts of all beings. Even the Asura emperor, Surapadma, who had no reason to fear anyone, could not escape the feeling, and neither could Tarakasura. Simhamukha was calm as he was deeply engrossed in his daily prayer, standing in front of a gigantic idol of Mahakali. He was startled violently by all the offerings in front of Mahakali falling off one by one. The idol started to grow, glow with heat and look horrifically gruesome.

Mahadeva's face took a new turn as it transformed into the Tatpurusha aspect of Sadasiva, facing east. It glowed like gold. He was Maheswara now. The air heated up, became thick and rose to an unbearable temperature as Indra, Vayu, Agni and Narada fainted, as did the rest of the beings in the multiverse. It was this head from which Maya sprang forth and started conducting the multiverse.

Another head sprouted facing west, right behind Maheswara. Tremors shook the earth. Trees fell. Mountains split. The face was purest white in colour. Thus, Satyojata came into being. This was the creator aspect, the aspect that assigned creation duties to Brahma after educating him on the how, why, what, when and who, as well as the rules to follow.

This was followed by the sprouting of another head in the

northern direction. This face was as red as a gigantic dying star. Water began to boil across all oceans, including the Milky Ocean, which was the residence of Mahavishnu. This aspect maintained the multiverse and it was this aspect that educated Vishnu on the duties of protecting righteousness. Vamadeva came into being.

After that, a head started to spring in the southern direction. It was by far the most horrific of faces one can possibly imagine. It was blue in colour, breathed fire and looked like it was going to ensure that nothing would be left in existence once it had its way. It was Aghora, who discharged the duties of destruction and instructed Rudra on how to perform the same. Nandi fainted.

Next, a head sprouted facing upwards. The face was shiny and reflected all light and heat like a diamond. This was Ishana. This granted liberation to souls after complete destruction by Aghora. This was the most powerful face in all the multiverse in the current creation. This was Sadasiva himself, in an active form, from which the rest of the multiverse came to be.

No one, barring Brahma, Vishnu and Parvati, was left standing. They could neither see the brilliance nor take their eyes off it. They believed that they had seen the complete magnificence from which everything that ever existed has come to be.

The multiverse shook again as it did every time a new face sprouted. Even the trio could not bear the heat or illumination any more and they turned to move away.

A new face, unknown to all, sprouted facing downward, inside the being in front of them. This was Athomukha; it faced Parabrahmam itself and was in constant bliss due to being in constant touch with it. This would be the face that would be left at the end of it all, manifest as Mahakaal, killing off time and space. It is upon the manifestation of this face on the outside that Kali would elevate to become Mahakali. An energy, emitted from the chest of the being with five heads—the chest that housed the sixth head—entered Parvati: her body rose in the air, shook violently and she fell as if dead. Her anklet with nine gems fell off. Vishnu and Brahma ran to her to check on her but when they reached out to touch her, they were thrown back by the immense heat emanating from her body. She floated up by herself. She was glowing as if she was an ember. Her face was radiant, and she was smiling. Brahma and Vishnu understood that Shakti had entered her being and she was who she was always meant to be.

The eyes of the being were still closed. It opened its eyes, all three of them, in all six of its heads. Primordial energy, in the form of cosmic fire, blasted from the third eye in each of the heads. The eyes had not been open even for a fraction of a second when all the water evaporated , and the ice melted and evaporated as well. The fire that burnt for the few miniscule fractions of time formed six balls.

Vamadeva, Satyojata and Maheswara then restored the multiverse to what it had been before. The heads disappeared. To all beings barring the three who were witness, it was like a bad dream. For the Asuras, it was a bad omen.

Divine women sprang up from the nine gems of the anklet, and at the sight of Shiva in his transition from his powerful form, became pregnant. Angered, Parvati cursed them to carry the children forever without delivering them. Parvati too would have done the same, unable to bear the brilliance of Shiva, had she not been the powerful Shakti's aspect.

Indra, Vayu, Agni, Narada and Nandi woke up. Brahma instructed Agni to carry the six balls of cosmic fire and deposit them in Sara Vana as Shiva had earlier instructed. Mahavishnu, with an all-knowing smile, ordered Vayu to accompany him and follow the route of the Ganges to reach Sara Vana. As ordered, they took the blessings of Brahma and Vishnu before they left.

Quickly after that Indra, Narada and Brahma left for Satyaloka as Vishnu did to Vaikunta.

Agni and Vayu took off with the balls in Agni's hand. Though initially confident of handling any fire being Agni, he started to feel fatigue, something a Deva or Vasu should never feel, thanks to Amrut. As he went on, it became unbearable. He was sweating profusely, again something someone who has consumed Amrut should not experience. After a point, having reached halfway to the Ganges, Agni was about to faint. He handed the balls to Vayu and fell out of the sky.

Vayu too did his best, before suffering the same fate as Agni. He was, however, successful in reaching the Ganges, where the balls of fire dropped. As soon as the fireballs touched the Ganges, the goddess of the river, unable to bear the heat, ran to Vishnu, who asked her to deposit the same in Sara Vana as Shiva had instructed.

The Ganges rolled down doubly fast, taking the balls of fire and finally dumping them in the lake in Sara Vana. Lotuses emerged where the fire balls were dumped and the lake glowed like it was housing six suns. All the trees in the forest soon bore fruit. The flowers blossomed. The forest became lively.

Parvati wanted someone of her own. Shiva would be having a child of his own soon. Even the women who were her gems were pregnant. She also felt powerful enough, now that Shakti had entered her, to attempt and create a child of her own.

Having taken no cognizance of the events that had unfolded, not unlike the rest of the universe, Indra was back to being his grumpy self. Even when he asked Narada or Brahma, the former told him that he was equally clueless, while the latter told him that there were no words to describe his experience. All he could tell Indra was that he was in pure bliss, having realized who Mahadeva truly was. Indra went to Vishnu and said, 'O lord! Mahadeva is still sitting in useless meditation. Is there any relief for me? If not, please slay me.'

Vishnu replied, 'Mind your words, Sakra. Your mind is too narrow to grasp the glory of Sadasiva. His penance for millennia bore fruits that are beyond the reach of your infantile mind and imagination. The scene Brahma and I witnessed and were blessed to be a part of cannot be grasped by anyone's imagination, let alone words. Do not come to me anymore, for the only person who can help you has already done it. Only after you realize it will the doors of Vaikunta be open for you.'

Indra left Vaikunta with a long face, to go back to his hiding spot in Kailash, for which he was not even grateful.

Ganesha

*P*arvati left for her cavern in Kailash. She sat down in contemplation and quietly slipped into a trance. She had no idea how long she was in that state. After a long time, she woke up, much calmer. She saw that there was some mud in the mountains: thanks to the melting of ice, evaporation of water and later restoration by the being that embodies Mahadeva, the mud pile was rich, soft and malleable.

She formed a small cone and transformed it into a boy-like figure. As she blew over the figure to dry it, it came to life. The clay figure bowed to her. She was happy and blessed it. As soon as she blessed it, the clay figure transformed into a beautiful, handsome and strong boy.

'Mother!' addressed the boy. The rush of joy Parvati felt at being addressed as mother by a child led her into the ecstasy that only a mother can know. She was in the most blissful state that sages acquire after centuries of penance. It was a joy so high and pure that no matter how many words one uses to describe it, it would still not do any justice. Tears of joy ran down her cheeks.

'Son!' she cried as she hugged the boy.

'I will take a bath for it is time for prayer. You will pray with me too, my son. Guard the entrance and let no one inside until

I come,' said Parvati to the boy.

'I will do as you ordered, Mother!' said the boy as she left.

Unknown to them, Shiva had woken up and asked Nandi to summon Parvati, as the nine gem women had implored Mahadeva for mercy. He wanted to ask Parvati to lift their curse. As Nandi was about to enter, he was stopped by a little boy. Nandi scoffed at him and tried to enter, but the boy, having been breathed to life by Shakti, threw Nandi off with a single punch. This was something Nandi did not even imagine was possible.

Nandi rushed at the boy, full of wrath and anger like a bull that has seen red. The boy side-stepped Nandi and threw him off so hard that he fell at the gates of Mahadeva's cavern. The sight of his beloved Nandi falling in front of his cavern angered Mahadeva. He stormed outside and asked Nandi what had happened, and Nandi narrated the story to him.

Upon hearing of the presence of a boy in his beloved Parvati's private quarters, Mahadeva went there. The boy stopped Mahadeva. The small boy who had just come into existence stopped the lord of time and space who will never cease to exist.

'Who are you? What are you doing here?' asked Mahadeva.

'I am Parvati's son,' replied the boy valiantly and went on to ask Mahadeva, 'Who are you?'

'I am Parvati's husband. I am your father. Let me in,' said Mahadeva.

'My mother has ordered me not to let anyone in. I will not let you or anyone in,' said the boy defiantly.

'You will incur my wrath. You are a little boy. Do not lose your life standing in the way and blocking a husband from entering the quarters of his beloved wife,' said Mahadeva.

'I only know of my mother. She is everything. Unless she tells me you are my father and that you should be allowed to enter at will, you will not take a step forward,' said the boy.

Though he was initially amused, this angered Shiva. He took a step forward and the boy materialized a staff with a ball at its head and banged Shiva's feet. The ball imploded to pieces upon impact. This did not deter the boy, for he kept producing staff after staff and started attacking Shiva all over. He could not make Mahadeva take a step back, though. Then the boy ran far back and rushed like a mad elephant at Shiva, hitting Shiva's chest with his head.

Shiva took a step back upon impact. Seeing this, Nandi rushed towards the boy, who threw Nandi down the mountain in one swing. Shiva, angered at the plight of Nandi, took his Trisula and threw it at the boy, taking his head off.

'Mother!' cried the boy's head as it hit the ground. The voice echoed in Satyaloka and Vaikunta. Brahma and Vishnu rushed in, as did Parvati.

Parvati, in grief and wrath upon seeing the lifeless head and twitching body, exploded in fury, taking a scary, gigantic form with ten arms, each wielding a fiery weapon.

She rushed at the Trimurtis but stopped when she saw Mahadeva, her husband, bow to her with folded hands. She saw Mahavishnu and Brahma do the same and then realized who she was, what she was doing and what she had become. It happened when it was supposed to happen, triggered by a complex cause–effect cycle that is beyond mortal comprehension.

She restored herself to Parvati's form and cried out, holding her son's head. The body of the boy had stopped twitching and his life was now extinguished.

Mahadeva turned to Vishnu and requested him to go eastward and get the head of the first animal he could find. Vishnu complied. He went towards the east and saw a gigantic white elephant who was the patriarch of Airavata's family, the only other white elephant that could fly. It was the wise forefather and one of the wisest beings that was not one of the Trimurtis. Vishnu paid due respect to him and told him the circumstances. The elephant bowed to Vishnu gladly, who then took its head off and rushed to Kailash.

Mahadeva then asked Brahma to attach the head of the elephant to the body of the boy, as he had done with Daksha. Mahadeva breathed life into the being. The boy, now with the head of an elephant, bowed to Parvati.

'Bless me, O divine mother!' said the elephant-headed boy. Parvati was overcome by emotion and hugged the boy tightly.

'Gajanan!' called Mahadeva. The boy prostrated before him and did the same to Brahma and Vishnu. They all blessed him.

'Parvati, your son, created by you, will be not only be our first son, but will also be the first in any and every holy event. He will have the power to create and remove obstacles. Any work by anyone, which does not begin without paying due respect to him, will be marred by innumerable obstacles which can only be removed by worshipping him. Having defeated Nandi, he will also be the chief of staff for my Ganas and will be called Ganapati and Ganesha. His name will become synonymous with auspiciousness.

'The right to first Avir (share in offerings) in any yagna, that was mine so far, will now go to him. Irrespective of the aim and purpose of the yagna, unless the first Avir is offered to him, it will fail. Worshipping him will give the fruit of worshipping you and me together. Having inherited the head of the wisest being, he will be known for his wisdom. Success and wisdom will be two of his attributes that define him,' said Mahadeva.

Mahavishnu, in his turn, said, 'Sister! My nephew will forever be associated with wealth and prosperity. Wherever he is worshipped and given first respect, my wife, Lakshmi will take residence there. Worshipping him will give them the same benefit as worshipping me and Lakshmi together.'

Brahma followed suit and said, 'Parvati, as with Vishnu, wherever he is worshipped, Saraswati's blessing is by default ordained there. No work of literature will commence without his form being the first word that is being written. If not, that work will not attain success. He will become synonymous with all knowledge that is in existence.'

Having been blessed thus by the Trimurtis, Parvati was filled with joy.

'Parvati,' said Mahadeva. She looked up. 'Remove the curse that you placed on the nine gems who became women and fell pregnant. It is all happening for a cause and you, being the holy mother now, should be able to see it.'

Parvati closed her eyes and as if struck by lightning, she could see everything and beyond the cause–effect cycle. Her tears vanished. She no longer was mere Parvati, daughter of Himavat and wife of Shiva. She had realized her true potential; she was Mahashakti, counterpart of Mahadeva.

She summoned the nine gem women and said, 'Your curse will be lifted the moment you set eyes on my son, for whom your sons will not only be mere brothers but his shadow, who will support him when the time comes.' They all bowed to her and left. Mahavishnu and Brahma left as well, as Mahadeva, Mahashakti and Ganesha went to their residence.

Kritikas

*C*ompletely dissatisfied and desolate, as Indra was seething at his own impotence and the lack of intent to help him and restore him to the position of Prajapati, a horde of sages came to meet him.

'Sakra!' said the head among the sages. 'There is something happening in Sara Vana from where we hail. The lake there, where we do our daily ablutions, was on fire. All the trees in the forest, without waiting for their time, bore fruit. All the flowers have blossomed at the same time. These are out of the ordinary and seem to be a bad omen. Being the protector of sages, even if you are not Prajapati, it is your duty to protect us.'

'O great seer!' replied Indra, 'I am, right now, at my weakest, as weak as possible for a Deva to ever be. My condition is desolate. I have been abandoned by Mahadeva, Mahavishnu and Brahma. I am not being helped by anyone, and I am not in a position to help anyone. There used to be yagnas performed to honour and favour me, from which I sought power, but that too has ceased. I am not in a position to fight even a human, let alone a being capable of setting lakes on fire and blossoming an entire forest. Whatever it is, it is beyond my ability to destroy.'

'You cannot disown your responsibilities, Sakra. You are bound by duty to do your best, irrespective of it being enough or not,' said the sage.

'O sage, I will summon the last of my powers and send it out to investigate and, if possible, destroy the force that you saw in the forest. In return, I want you to secretly perform a yagna, without the knowledge of the Asuras, to empower me even more, so that I can discharge the duties that have been assigned to me and that you have come to remind me of,' said Indra.

'Sakra, we agree to your request. We will initiate a yagna once the force that is in the forest has been taken care of. We are afraid to go back to the forest as long as it is there,' said the sage.

Indra closed his eyes, chanted a mantra and summoned six women. They were very beautiful but also looked very dangerous.

'Go to the forest, find and destroy the being that is the cause of the changes in the Sara Vana,' ordered Indra as he sat down, having lost the last few bits of his power.

The Kritika sisters, as ordered, ventured into the forest.

The forest was lively and happy, and it looked beautiful, serene and lovely. The fragrance of flowers was carried by the wind across the forest. The sisters began to wonder if the cause behind this change could actually be evil. As they entered deeper and deeper into the forest, they saw a bright light from afar. They ventured closer to the light, each transforming into their fearsome form. When they reached the lake's shore, they were stunned.

Inside six lotuses were six beautiful babies, with lush black hair, green eyes, a full set of perfect teeth, and red palms and feet. Their smiles could melt any heart and transform it into pure love. The same happened to the Kritika sisters. They forgot how they came to be, what they had come for, and took it upon themselves to nurse and bring up the babies, which they believed were coincidentally six in number. Their maternal instincts kicked in as soon as they saw the babies, and they took them from the lotuses and nursed them. They took care of the babies as if they were their own, with pure love, adoration and a protective maternal instinct.

The sages did not return to the forest for they could still see the same symptoms persist. Indra was too weak to even care about what happened to the babies or the Kritika sisters. The babies started to grow up in peace.

Cheyyon

One fine day, the Kritika sisters were busy playing with the six babies, who had grown up to be toddlers, in Sara Vana.

In Kailash, Parvati and Shiva were engaged in conversation, while Ganesha was busy playing with his pet Mooshika, a rat. As they talked, their attention went to what Ganesha was doing.

Parvati turned to Shiva and asked, 'Is the time right, my lord?'

Shiva smiled, 'Yes, my beloved Uma. Let us go.' They asked Ganesha to take care of Kailash, and being the chief, he gladly obliged. Having been blessed by all the Trimurtis, Ganesha knew and had the ability to understand and see how things will unfold.

Shiva and Parvati appeared in Sara Vana. The Kritika sisters were initially afraid for their children's safety and picked them up, fearing that their children were Asuras whom Mahadeva and Parvati had come to slay. The toddlers however were filled with joy and smiled radiantly.

'Do not fear, O Kritika! We are not here to slay your children. We are here to take our child home,' said Parvati.

'No, these are our children. We brought them up. We will not let anyone harm them. We will lose our lives before you take them from us,' said the Kritika sisters. One of them took the six children away, while the others formed a shield in front of them.

'Kritikas, the child you have is no ordinary one. He is born of me. He is my son. You were made to come to bring them up and protect the child. Do not forget why Indra first sent you here and what task you took upon yourself. It is all happening according to destiny. Your role in the play is over and you have played it splendidly. The child has been taken care of well. For your crucial role, as a reward, the six of you will shine in the night sky as a constellation,' said Mahadeva.

'O supreme one! Which of the six children are you referring to? We cannot bear to leave all of them. Take the child that belongs to you and we will live with the rest,' said the eldest sister.

'There is but one child,' said Parvati, kneeling down.

The six toddlers ran into Parvati's arms. As soon as she hugged all the six of them together, their bodies merged. The child now had twelve arms, six heads and eighteen eyes. She lifted him and he shone brightly, his face red and luminous.

Shiva called the child to him. 'He is my son. The six forms were six aspects of him, emerging from me. They had to fully and independently develop, without one compromising or sacrificing the other. He is Cheyyon, the red-hued one,' said Mahadeva.

'But he will forget us, Mahadeva, if we were to become constellations. We want to be with him, if not as mothers, as servants,' said the sisters.

Suddenly, Sara, the goddess of the forest appeared and said, 'The child is my son too, Mahadeva. Kindly let him reside here.'

The goddess Ganges appeared and made a similar request. Agni appeared and made a similar request as well, while Parvati too insisted on being his mother.

Mahadeva smiled at the child and said, 'What do you say, my son?' as he set the child on the ground.

Cheyyon stood up and said, 'Kindly do not argue. It is because of all your contributions that I am who I am and where I am today. As I have been put together into one being instead of being six by my mother Parvati, I will be Skanda. As I have been brought up by my six beloved mothers the Kritikas, I will be Kartikeya. As I was born in the Sara Vana, I will be Saravana. As the Ganges carried me in her womb and deposited me in the lake, I will be Kumara. As I was carried by Agni to the Ganges, I will be Mahasena. As I was conceived and created by the supreme lord's supreme form, I will be Guha. As the forest was where I took my current form from being a mere ball of fire that emanated from Shiva, Sa-Ra-Va-Na-Ba-Va will be my beej mantra. As I was nurtured, nursed and brought up by the Kritika sisters, the day of their constellation will be my holy day and anyone who worships me on their day will get twice the benefit as worshipping me on other days,' said Cheyyon.

The audience was shocked and surprised at the erudite response and solution provided by the toddler. The six sisters hugged the child and left for the skies to shine as constellations. Ganga, Sara and Agni left too, as Shiva, Parvati and Skanda left for Kailash. The sages came back and conducted the yagnas as they had promised, once the place was back to normal, to empower Indra.

Meru

*K*ailash was joyful with all the children, including Ganesha and the Nava Kumaras (nine boys), along with Guha. There was always fun, frolic, laughter, teasing and crying. Once, Guha teased Ganesha a bit too much and was sent out till evening as a punishment by Parvati.

Guha, however, flew around happily without a destination, looking to explore the universe. He travelled north to see the world that resided upwards of his home, Kailash. It looked beautiful and pleasant, and everything was pristine. Still unaware of people other than those he had met in Kailash, he was filled with joy at the sight of so many people going about doing their work.

As he flew around, Guha saw the beautiful waves rising from the ocean. Being his mischievous and innocent self, he asked his peacock to drink up as much as possible. The peacock did his bidding and went on to drink up the entire Milky Ocean. He mounted the peacock again and flew off northward until he came across Mount Meru. Not knowing what it actually was, he felt that the peak was higher than his home, Kailash, so he went ahead and broke off the top of it, reducing it to a smaller size and throwing away the broken bit southward.

Upon seeing the Milky Ocean dried up and Mount Meru broken, the sages in Sara Vana, who had never left the place except for it was occupied by Guha, again ran to Indra and said, 'Sakra! We had already warned you about the new changes that happened in Sara Vana being a bad omen. You did not listen to us. Now Mount Meru is broken and is no longer holy. The oceans are dried up as well. A demon is out loose, destroying everything. Come and fight it. We have done our yagna as we promised, and you should be powerful enough now to take on it, as it appears to be a child.'

Indra felt powerful as well and wanted to see how strong he

had become. After the yagna, he felt rejuvenated, and felt that the child demon would be a good place to start to test his strength. He summoned Vayu, who had never gone back after the wedding, and managed to evade Sura thanks to being safely hosted in the vicinity of Kailash. Accompanied by the sages, both rushed to Mount Meru, where Guha was wreaking havoc with his childish play.

'Stop! Who are you?' asked Indra authoritatively, feeling powerful and good after a long time.

'Stop! Who are you?' repeated Guha in a mocking tone.

'I am Sakra, king of the Devas, protector of sages, bestower of gifts and ruler of the universe. I am Indra. Surrender to me and I will spare your life,' said Indra, standing heroically as a symbol of courage.

'I am Sakra,' mocked Guha, mimicking Indra's heroic posture and then giggling uncontrollably.

'How dare you mock me?' bellowed Sakra.

Guha did what any sweet child would do, repeating what Sakra said in his own sweet voice. This angered Indra to no end. He, along with Vayu, rushed with full force at the child, taking him head on, but the child did not even move an inch. All the force that Vayu and Indra physically exerted was rendered useless.

'Stop tickling me,' said Guha, laughing loudly.

Vayu got angry and created a gigantic storm that howled across the mountains. The storm moved towards the child, uprooting everything in its way. As it got near, Guha merely opened his mouth and swallowed the storm, letting out a burp at the end. Having used his best and most powerful weapon, Vayu's face dropped.

Indra, summoning his power and control over lightning and thunder, summoned dark clouds. Guha looked up, wondering what this strange phenomenon was, having never experienced rain in Kailash. It started to rain heavily and Guha danced happily in the rain.

'Drink up, peacock. You wanted water, didn't you?' said Guha and the peacock obliged.

Indra directed lightning towards Guha. Seeing the flash of lights from the sky, Guha laughed gleefully, clapping his hands. Indra then directed all his energy to land the lightning bolt on the child, accompanied by deafening thunder.

As the lightning bolt neared, Guha captured it and looked at it with wonder, smiling all the while. He then proceeded to bend the lightning bolt to make a ring and wore it on his finger. Seeing his best defeated, Indra's face sank like Vayu's. The sages who had complained, were aghast.

Guha turned to Indra and smiled, asking, 'Are you done, king of the Devas, protector of sages, bestower of gifts, ruler of the universe?' Indra bowed before the child and said, 'Yes, my lord. You are far more powerful than I am. I concede defeat.' Vayu followed suit, and so did the sages.

Hearing all the commotion, Narada arrived. 'What are you doing, Indra? Have you lost your mind? Do you dare to take on Guha, the son of Mahadeva?' Narada then turned to Guha, 'Kindly forgive him, benevolent one. Neither does he know who you are nor does he understand your power.'

Immediately, Guha abandoned his childlike form and stood up like a giant, shocking and scaring all except Narada. Skanda then started to grow in stature, taking the Vishwaroopa form. The sages, Vayu, Indra and Narada were blinded by the brilliance of the cosmic form, unable to even look in that direction. Narada, on behalf of all, said, 'O kind lord, I request you to bless us with eyes that are capable of seeing your magnificence.'

'So be it!' thundered a voice.

With new eyes, they looked at the gigantic form in front of them. Even his hair held complete universes with progenitors and protectors, life going on in full swing in each of them. They tried to look up at his face and were blinded by the brilliance and closed their eyes. Having realized whom they were standing in front of, they all prostrated before him.

As they got up, in front of them was a sweet child with a beautiful smile, sitting on a peacock.

Narada!

*N*arada, along with Guha, came back to Kailash. He apprised the inhabitants, other than Shiva, of the events that had happened, and they were enthralled at the brilliance of their child. Ganesha proudly hugged his brother while the Nava Kumaras prostrated before him. Parvati kissed his forehead.

Nandi came in at that moment and said, 'Narada Muni! Mahadeva summons you.'

Narada took leave of his audience and went to the cavern where Mahadeva was meditating. He prostrated before him and took his blessings.

'Perform a yagna, my beloved Narada. Perform a yagna for the betterment of the world,' said Mahadeva.

'As you order, my lord, I will at once commence a yagna,' replied Narada. Mahadeva blessed him with a smile on his face.

Narada, at the word of Mahadeva, went to what was left of Mount Meru and started a yagna. It was a simple but sincere affair. Upon hearing of the news, Indra, Vayu, the Sara Vana sages, Saptrishi and everyone who could possibly join, came forward to contribute and participate in the same.

Surapadma too did not mind the yagna, for it was happening in the no-war zone of Mount Meru, and also because the yagna was for a good cause from which he too benefitted.

The yagna started simply, with the fire being fed with ghee, milk, herbs and Dharpas (sacred grass used in Homam) while everyone chanted the Gayatri Mantra. As the yagna progressed and the fire began to grow, Narada started to chant a mantra that would empower the world and make it safe from destruction, irrespective of who was ruling it. To strengthen it, he decided to make it unconquerable. As a part of his mantra, he used the word 'Ajai' ('Jai' is victory, 'Ajai' is something which cannot be won over) but unfortunately, pronounced it as 'Aja' (ram).

No sooner than he finished his mantra, a gigantic ram jumped out of the fire, its nostrils breathing fire. It had sharp horns and sharper teeth. The ram was looking for a fight and started to chase everyone in and around the yagnashala. Everyone ran helter-skelter and, as always, Indra was the first one to get to safety. Narada, in fear, called out Mahadeva's name as he rushed towards Kailash.

On his way to the cavern, he was stopped by Ganesha, Veerabahu and Guha, who asked him what the problem was. Narada narrated it in an elaborate manner and all three of them laughed. Narada wondered what was so funny and asked them so.

Ganesha asked, 'You forgot something, didn't you?' to which Narada, with a confused expression said, 'I followed all the rules, O wise one. Enlighten me as to what my mistake was.'

'You forgot that Mahadeva had decreed that the first offering should always go to Ganesha, the first among equals. You started the yagna without offering salutations to the Lord of Auspiciousness,' said Veerabahu.

'I apologize, my lord,' said Narada immediately. 'This will not happen again. But there is a huge ram now that is destroying everything in its path. Kindly help us, lest the yagna started to save and protect the world should end up being the cause of its destruction!'

'Veerabahu,' said Guha, 'Go and fetch me the ram.'

Veerabahu bowed and left. The ram that had been causing havoc all around, stopped and stared at Veerabahu. Their eyes met. The ram first took an aggressive stance, preparing to charge. The sages, Indra, Vayu and Narada, who were watching from their hiding places, were scared as it started to charge.

'Skanda!' thundered Veerabahu, stamping his foot hard on the earth. Feeling and hearing the impact, the ram stopped dead in its tracks, went to Veerabahu and bowed. Veerabahu held the ram by its horns and took it to Kailash and gave it to Guha. Ganesha and Guha played with it. Guha took it as his playmate as well as Vahana for when he did not want to fly around on his peacock. It was all a play by Mahadeva to show the world and his children who they really were.

Jnanaphala

*T*ime rolled by at its usual pace and the children grew up. One day, Narada got a fruit, divine by nature, which would give the eater all the knowledge in the universe, including Brahma Gyan (the secretive, complex, supreme knowledge of how everything came to be).

Being a wise sage, Narada took the fruit to Kailash. Giving the fruit to Mahadeva, he said, 'O divine one! I got this fruit by accident. This fruit, upon consumption, is capable of giving the eater divine knowledge. Such knowledge in the wrong hands could prove to be dangerous. Being the wisest of beings, I request you to consume it and make it unattainable, except by your grace.'

Mahadeva, with a smile, replied, 'Wise sage! The existence of the fruit, by itself, means that it is for someone without the knowledge. Besides, as someone who already possesses the same, eating the fruit would render the purpose of existence of such a fruit futile. Parvati, mother of my children, would you like to consume it?'

Parvati, who also now had the grasp of knowledge with realization, understood what Mahadeva meant and said, 'As addressed by you, O holy one, and being a mother, I insist that this fruit should belong to the next generation. Our sons should be the ones who can consume it and gain from it.'

Upon hearing the words, both Ganesha and Guha rushed towards their mother, asking for the fruit. Nandi suggested that the fruit should be cut into two halves and given to both. Narada interjected, saying, 'We cannot cut knowledge in half. Half knowledge is the most dangerous thing in the world. No matter who consumes it, they should consume it in full.' Mahadeva agreed.

'I would rather have my children playing than one of them crying for the fruit,' said Parvati, asking Narada to take it back.

'Let us have a competition. Such a divine fruit must be earned and not given,' said Mahadeva, to which everyone there agreed.

'Skanda! Ganesha! Between the two of you, the one who goes around the universe and comes back to me first earns the fruit,' ordered Mahadeva.

Guha gleefully said, 'I will complete my journey and be back first. I have already travelled northward. I will travel south, east and west, complete my journey and win the fruit. Good luck, fat Ganesha, on riding your Mooshika and completing the task!' Guha immediately took off on his peacock, leaving Ganesha bewildered.

Crying would not work, for Mahadeva was the judge. Going around the universe on his Mooshika, a rat, was not a possibility either. He sat down, closed his eyes for a few moments and then got up. Meanwhile, Guha, on his peacock, travelled at the speed of thought, covering east and west.

'Father! Mother! Bless me as I commence my journey!' said Ganesha as he bowed to them. They blessed him. He then took three rounds around them and came back to his original position and said, 'Give me the fruit, for I have won.' This confused the audience but Mahadeva and Parvati understood what he meant.

'But how? You have not left the place,' said Narada.

'Wise sage! To children, their parents are the universe. To the universe, they are the parents. When my parents and the universe are synonymous, with the latter coming from the former, having gone around them not once but thrice, do I not deserve the fruit?' asked Ganesha. Having heard such profound explanation from a mere child, Narada bowed to Ganesha.

Mahadeva and Parvati looked at each other and Parvati proceeded to give the fruit to Ganesha, who went on to eat it. Skanda, at that precise moment, entered Kailash. The sight of his beloved mother and father giving the fruit to Ganesha, who in no possibility could have completed the task, made him angry.

'Was this all a trick? Was this done to get rid of me so that the fruit can be given to your favourite son? I am grateful to you, my parents, for letting me know where I stand in terms of preference, be it love or fruit,' said Skanda, storming out of Kailash.

Ganesha, having eaten the fruit and having gained all the wisdom, saw the reason behind the game.

Parvati rushed to console her angry child, explaining to him what had happened, even though she knew why this was happening, but he would not hear any of it. Mahadeva let him go, for he had a purpose behind the play. Guha climbed the peacock and left Kailash, flying towards the Asura empire unknowingly.

Idumba

Still angry at the perceived stepchild treatment from his divine parents, Guha was flying on his peacock. He did not notice when he passed over Krauncha and crossed into the Asura empire. Nobody in the Asura empire cared for a child flying in, as they didn't for a small, short and nondescript sage.

Agastya had left for the south and he was busy spreading the word of god as well as changing the topology for better. He took each and every event, as well as every challenge, as a direction given by Mahadeva for him to act on. He did not worry about taking the wrong action either. For him, his being, the events and challenges he faced, the solutions that he came up with, were all orchestrated by Mahadeva. Agastya also had a student, Idumba, a Rakshasa, who had first opposed him and then submitted to him upon realizing his true potential.

Agastya, along with Ganesha, changed the course of the then arrogant Kaveri River to flow southward. At one point, Goddess Kaveri mocked the sage for his appearance. This was common to him, but he had been sent on a job and he was keen on doing it. Agastya, using his yogic powers, imprisoned her in his Kamandalam and took her on his journey southward, drying out the river in its then course. When he went to perform his daily ablutions in a pond, leaving his Kamandalam on the shore, a crow pushed it off, leaving the river, Kaveri, in its current course. When Agastya confronted the crow, it transformed into Ganesha. Being someone with a not-so-regular appearance, he identified with him instantly. Upon knowing who Ganesha was, he prostrated before him in all humility and received blessings as well as instructions from him.

As a part of his task, he got the two pieces of Meru that had fallen off thanks to the antics of Guha, to be placed in the south. The two peaks were named Shaktigiri and Sivagiri, and Agastya had Idumba carry them tied to a tree on his shoulders. When they came to the right spot, Agastya told Idumba to take some rest while he went to do his daily ablutions.

It was at this moment that Guha ventured into the territory. Upon seeing a peak of exalted holiness that was familiar to him, Guha decided to make it his home. He sat there and started to meditate. As soon as he sat down there, his anger vanished, and he became calm again.

Agastya came back and asked Idumba to pick up his load, as they were about to leave. Idumba tried to pick up the hills but Shaktigiri would not even budge. The Rakshasa shrunk back to his original size and climbed up to the top. Upon seeing a little boy sitting in ochre robes, Idumba said to him, 'Get off the hill!'

Guha did not respond and this angered Idumba even more, so he rushed at Guha, who opened his eyes and stepped out of the way, leaving Idumba to slip and fall. Enraged, Idumba said, 'Good that you got up. Now, leave the hill. I need to carry it off as my teacher ordered.'

'This is my hill now. I have chosen this as my abode. Leave this and you will leave with your life,' said Guha.

'You do not know who you are talking to. I am a student of Agastya, the great sage. I am a powerful Rakshasa as well. You are a small child. I do not want to harm you,' said Idumba.

'You do not know who I am either. Without the knowledge of each other, there is no way anyone can know who is more powerful. If you are willing to find out, I am ready. Do not hold back on account of my appearance. This is not the first time you have judged people on their appearance,' said Guha. The response shocked Idumba, for this was not the first time he heard those words. This experience was similar to the one he had with Agastya. Idumba, humbly, bowed.

'I apologize,' said Idumba. 'Can I know who you are?'

'He is the son of Mahadeva and Mahashakti, brother of Ganesha, whom you were fortunate to meet when he released Kaveri. He is divinity personified,' said Agastya, who had come to see what happened to his student.

Idumba prostrated himself before the child. On seeing Agastya, Guha felt a rush of immense joy. Agastya felt the same. Guha and Agastya hugged each other, and Agastya asked Idumba to take some rest for they had to have a discussion.

Agastya and Guha had a major discourse. Agastya was instructed by Guha with divine knowledge and given instructions on how to obtain various Siddhis, alchemy and medicinal knowledge. In addition to that, he received knowledge of the perfect grammar of the language of the region, Tamizh, starting the Siddha culture and a rich Tamizh tradition that was to pervade, transform and morph the Asura empire.

Through a debate with Agastya, Guha understood that there is always a reason behind everything that happens to one and Mahadeva was not someone who tells his chosen ones what to do, but directs them through a chain of events. Guha's anger subsided completely. He then summoned Idumba.

'Idumba, I am impressed with your devotion to the word of your teacher. Ask for a boon,' said Guha.

'O great one! Whoever carries a Kavadi (a simple structure with a long wooden rod carrying two equal weights on both sides, balancing each other like the one used by Idumba to carry the hills) and comes and prays to you here should get whatever their heart desires,' requested Idumba.

'Your heart is pure. Even when you could have asked for any boon, you chose to ask for something for the people. I bless you with what you asked. Your teacher is very fortunate to have you as your disciple.

'A disciple who follows the instruction of his teacher even at the risk of coming to harm fearlessly, is the ideal disciple. The teacher who protects, guides and instructs the student for the betterment of the student and the world, instead of using the student for their own welfare, is the ideal teacher. You are the perfect teacher and the perfect student. May you live long,' said Guha. Both of them prostrated before Guha, took his blessings and left.

Avvai

ℬorn deep inside Asura territory, Avvai was a sweet young girl born into a trading community among humans. They belonged to a race for whom the ruler did not matter much and who did not matter to the ruler either, if at all. Irrespective of being ruled by Asura or Deva or humans, their life had little change. They never were part of the wars for supremacy and nor did they care who their taxes went to, for it never went to their emperor directly. There were far too many intermediaries and they had never met anyone above a tax collector who was one among them. She was a young girl and having heard of Parvati's devotion to Mahadeva, she became devoted to him as well.

According to the custom of the day, girls were married off very young and when Avvai reached the age, she too was about to be married off. Detesting marriage, she ran to the nearby temple and hid behind Ganesha's statue, which was gigantic enough to hide anyone let alone a small girl. Ganesha's worship has been popularized and made famous by Agastya, which was a part of his mission and task in the Asura empire: to spread the worship of gods so as to remove fear from the hearts of the people under the Asuras. He was to be one among them, guiding them and preparing them for the changes that were to come.

Avvai stood in front of Ganesha and with her pure soul filled with love for the divine, prayed to him for something no one has ever asked for until then or since: old age. Ganesha, the benevolent god, appeared before her and blessed her to be old without further aging and with an incredibly long life which would end only when she chose, as well as wisdom and poetry, with the power to make her words come true when she chose to.

She thanked him profusely and took the life and garb of a wandering ascetic, roaming around from place to place in service of humanity and god, spreading his word and contributing to Agastya's cause and mission. One day, she was close to the hill which was now the abode of Guha.

'Salutations,' Avvai said, upon seeing a lonely tonsured boy in ochre garb, sitting on top of a hill all by himself. Guha returned the salutations to her, fully divining who she was and her purpose.

'Aren't you a child? Why are you in ochre robes? Why are you all by yourself? What is your name?' she asked him.

'Aren't you a child as well?' came the reply. Avvai, shocked that the child knew her story, said, 'Yes. But I am now an adult in people's eyes. I am, as a matter of fact, an elder. I do not carry any possessions that might cause people with evil intentions to come and harm me. You, on the other hand, are a child, a beautiful child. You might come to harm. If you do not mind, I can give you company and will be glad if you share your story with me.'

'I shall do so, for you look like a kind and benevolent soul. I have a wise father and a divine mother. I also have a brother. We all resided together. One day, we had a guest who got a fruit for us to consume, albeit it had to be consumed wholly by only one person. My parents said that we children should have it. However, they could not decide which of us should have it. My father said that the fruit has to be earned on such an occasion,' said Guha.

'A wise father, indeed. Teaching the children to earn, rather than giving them things they desire for free would lead to them being responsible and mature,' said Avvai.

'He told us that we both had to race. The one who raced around our house and came back first would get the fruit. I was indeed glad, for my brother was rather corpulent and there was no way he would beat me in a race, let alone around the house,' said Guha.

'That is wrong on your part. Appearances are deceptive. For someone who could see me for my real age in spite of my appearance, you should not have judged your brother for his,' said Avvai.

'I concede to that now. I did not have the maturity then to understand the same, even though I have the knowledge of everything. I started and raced ahead in full steam. But when I came back after completing the circle, I was shocked. My brother was not only given the fruit, but he had consumed it as well. It broke my heart,' said Guha.

'Which is only fair. What child would be able to bear the thought that their parents have given something to their sibling when they too wanted it? Further, the terms of the race were fulfilled only for you. When you were really the winner, they should not have given the fruit. But, I am sure your wise father did have his reasons. Did you confront him about the same?' asked Avvai.

'Yes. I did. My mother narrated to me what had happened. My brother took the blessings of my father and mother before he started the race and...' said Guha when Avvai interrupted, 'You too should have done the same. There is nothing bigger than the father and mother to a child. He is not only their house but also their universe. A child cannot know more than their father and mother until he gets a teacher.'

'Yes, you are right. I realize that now as well. He then went around them, not once but thrice, saying that they were not only his house but also his universe. He told them that I, his brother, had only gone around once, but he had gone around thrice. My father, upon hearing the argument, conceded and gave the fruit to him. I left my house in anger after that betrayal,' said Guha.

'Your father is right and you were wrong. Further, parents' words are not always what they mean. Sometimes, to get you to do something or teach you something important, they say and do things that appear like they hate you, but it has been done with the best interest for you in their hearts. You are blessed with a wise father, loving mother and an intelligent brother. You should go back,' said Avvai.

'I will go back after I meditate upon my mistakes. I will meditate further so that I attain the maturity which probably was the reason behind my father's actions: to make me mature and responsible,' said Guha.

'Very well. The next time I see you, I should see you with your family. Since you didn't give me your name, I will address you as

Muruga, the beautiful one,' said Avvai. Guha, taking her to be his grandmother, took her blessings in a state of irony.

On her way out of the hill into a town, a passer-by came and asked her where she was coming from. She pointed to the hill and said, 'Pazhani,' which in the language of the region, Tamizh, meant 'you are the fruit', as in the fruit of wisdom, addressing the only resident of the hill, Guha.

Muruga then sank into deep meditation, chanting 'Om Namah Shivaya', losing track of time, while Avvai continued her expedition, composing poetry.

Clan

*M*eanwhile, in Veeramahendrapuri, Surapadma was making the same mistake all emperors, including Indra, made: getting complacent. None of the events, including the presence of two new children in Kailash, mattered to him. He now firmly believed that unless Mahadeva came out himself, in person with his Trisula, he could not be defeated or killed. Agastya's presence, Vayu's escape, Indra's hiding were no longer things that bothered him.

He was the supreme ruler, still unopposed but bored with the activities that he was engaged in, be it torturing the Devas or administering the multiverse. Though he did not let his complacency interfere in his able and just administration for all other than the Devas, he was no longer the person who fought fearsome wars and took over everything. The only thing that did not change for Surapadma was his devotion to Mahadeva. Tarakasura had forsaken even that.

Tarakasura and Simhamukha too no longer cherished the role they played, though Simhamukha was as deeply engrossed in the worship of Kali, the divine mother, as ever. Krauncha and

Tarakasura became inseparable and had fun as much as they could. Along with Surapadma, all three of them were completely indulgent and dissipated. They even mocked Simhamukha if and when he advised them to live a life of righteousness, pointing out how soft he had become.

They also had multiple offsprings. Asurendran, the son of Tarakasura, was an adult and had learnt the arts of war, administration and Maya from their guru Sukhra, Brahma, Brihaspati and their grandmother Surasai. He had other sons, Vidyumali, Tarakaksha and Viryavana, but they were mere children. They lived with their grandmother to master the art of Maya.

Simhamukha's son, named Atisuran after his great grandfather, turned out to be a fine warrior but as dissipated as his uncles.

Banugopan, the son of Surapadma, turned out to be the finest of warriors, rivalled only by the three brothers. He also turned out to be the leader of the second generation, as the others looked up to him as Surapadma was looked up to by his brothers. Surapadma had two more sons of note, Agnimukha, the one with a face of fire, and Vajrabahu, the one who moved like lightning. He was aggressive and subordinate only to his father and his elder brother. He was also an expert practitioner of Tantric arts who, by pleasing Bhadrakali through sacrifices, got favours of equal weightage in return as and when he needed them. His other son, Iranian, was almost an ascetic who dedicated his life to the worship of the supreme lord.

Ajamukhi's two sons were also out in full force, destroying as many rishis and Devas as possible, taking out their mother's hatred on them on her behalf, as she had ordered.

On the administrative front, Surapadma segregated the individual circles surrounding Veeramahendrapuri to minor Asuras, as gifts for their valour, loyalty and ability

The sixth circle was ruled by Veerasinghan and the innermost circle was ruled by Yazhimugan. The second circle was ruled by

Ativeeran, son of Yazhimugan. His chief of staff was the able Gajamugan, who was dreaded not only for his prowess and loyalty, but also for his hatred of the Devas and his sadism.

Indrani was the only one that mattered to the Asuras. The four brothers, if you include Krauncha, had only one thought: vengeance for Ajamukhi's dismemberment. They somehow wanted to get Indrani and give her as a gift to Ajamukhi. They were disappointed to find out that she was in Kailash.

The situation of the Devas was no better, with the Asuras stepping up the torture on them to avenge Ajamukhi as Indrani had sought refuge in invincible Kailash. They were now being tortured by any and every Asura. It had become such a mundane activity that it had been relegated to the lowest order of the Asuras. The honour in being tortured, if there was one, was when they acted as target practice or as mute sparring partners for Asura royalty.

The Asura scientists were no longer the elite who were trying to find a way to extract their immortality and share the same with Asuras. They had become the least imaginative sadistic ones, who were more into satisfying their curiosity of what would happen if they were to do something to a Deva than someone with a purpose.

The Deva costume too went out of fashion and became democratized to the lower order Asuras, leading to mass production, which in turn led to more punishment for the Devas, as they were in demand in large quantities.

Jayanta's state was still the same and was the thing that pained the captive Devas the most. He still had not spoken a word, moved a muscle or even shown any sign of life. It was also the only thing that pained Sura, for he still had the same respect for Jayanta. Sura did the only thing he could to Jayanta, which was let him be and leave him alone, in solitude.

Time was a lost commodity for the oppressed in the multiverse.

Reunion

*M*uruga came back to Kailash on his ever-faithful peacock and set it free there. He had left as Guha, a small, immature, playful and naughty child, whose true nature was belied by his childish antics and immature attitude. He came back as Muruga, as named by Avvai, a responsible and mature adult, who knew the seriousness of his task, the vastness of his abilities, the depth of his divine knowledge and immense magnitude of his powers and had the knowledge and ability to use them wisely as well.

He was welcomed with a long, loving hug by Ganesha, who had gained all knowledge and wisdom, leaving behind his playfulness, upon consumption of the divine fruit. He had missed his brother and playmate a lot more than anyone else. Unlike his brother, he already had wisdom, thanks to the head from his father. The knowledge only added to it.

Parvati was besotted and tearful at the sight of her two children together again, not as playful children but as adults. Muruga, upon seeing his mother, ran and fell at her feet. She blessed him success in whatever he attempted as she kissed his forehead. The three of them went to the cavern where Mahadeva was meditating, after catching up among themselves.

Mahadeva opened his eyes gently and smiled at the sight of his son. His face showed Mahadeva what he wanted to see: the sign of enlightenment, the sign of having realized the ultimate truth. Muruga fell at Mahadeva's feet, who blessed him and then hugged him. He looked at his face proudly.

'I'm ready, Father. Give me my order and I will put an end to the vile Asuras, the progeny of Surasai, whose sole existence stems from the hatred of their stepbrothers, the Devas,' said Muruga.

'My lord, Guha is a small boy. He is a child. How can he take on those Asuras, whom the Devas who had Amrut cannot defeat, whom my brother Mahavishnu himself could not defeat? Please do not send our little one out like a lamb to slaughter,' said Parvati, desperate only as a mother would be, at the thought of not only being away from her child again, but also at the realization that he was keen to go out to face immense danger.

'Maya is clouding you again,' said Mahadeva. 'You are not merely the mother of this child or the other. You are Mahamaya. Why do you let yourself be pulled down over and again? Our son, Muruga, is invincible. He had to taste defeat once, as no one can ever be truly immune to defeat, including me and you. That is the law of the multiverse and being subjects of this multiverse, we are obliged to abide by its law and rule.

'Ganesha handed him that defeat when they went around the multiverse for the divine fruit of knowledge. Muruga, being a manifestation of my highest powers, is now invincible without exception. Just as Ganesha is synonymous with auspiciousness, Muruga is synonymous with victory. There is no force on the multiverse that can even harm his hair or stand his onslaught. The mere mention of his name alone will strike fear in the hearts of those who dare oppose him or oppress his devotees. His name alone will suffice as a shield against danger and evil, no matter how big.'

Parvati acknowledged what Mahadeva said, as did Ganesha.

Mahadeva then turned to Muruga and said, 'The time is not yet ripe. You still have some more work to do here, my son. When the time is right, I will give you the order. It is certain that it will be at your hands that the Asura race that emanated from Surasai will be obliterated.'

'I will do as you command, my father. I request your permission to go and visit my friends,' requested Guha, which Mahadeva allowed.

Muruga came out and was instantly hugged and lifted on their shoulders by the Nava Kumaras. They wanted to know everything, everything Muruga saw in the Asura empire, everyone he met, everything he learned and most importantly, if he had any orders for them.

Muruga shared the intricate details of the nature of the people, the landscape, the culture, the Asura empire that he had gathered himself and from conversations with Agastya who was sent south for precisely that task. He also informed them about Avvai and taught them the language, Tamizh, as well as its grammar. They absorbed it all without the realization that they were being prepared for a war in aspects other than actual warfare. As they were engaged in deep conversation, a figure passed by them.

Brahma

While the Nava Kumaras and Muruga were in conversation, Brahma paid a visit to Mahadeva about an urgent matter. He first crossed Nandi and they saluted each other. Then, he went past Ganesha, whom he was accustomed to seeing, and they too saluted each other. He then crossed Muruga, whom he did not recognize, as he had not created him and he had been away for a very long time. He merely went past him and the Nava Kumaras, though all of them saluted Brahma as they saw him.

Offended by the disrespect of Brahma, Veerabahu stood up, ready to punish Brahma. He was stopped by Muruga, who told him that all this was happening for a reason and that he would take care of everything.

Brahma finished his meeting and came out with a clearer head and a less confused face. He was stopped in his tracks by Veerabahu, upon the orders of Muruga.

'Why are you stopping me, Veerabahu? Do you need my blessings?' asked Brahma.

'No. I am stopping you upon the orders of my lord, Muruga,

son of Shiva,' said Veerabahu.

Brahma instantly realized his mistake. He quickly went to Muruga and saluted him. Muruga saluted him back and said, 'Your salutation is accepted, acknowledged and returned with due respect. However, your arrogance in not saluting or acknowledging me, the son of Mahadeva or the peerless Nava Kumaras is not forgiven, for we have not received an apology yet.'

'I apologize for not saluting you earlier, son of Mahadeva, for I did not recognize you,' said Brahma.

'Irrespective of that, it is the mark of a cultured man, let alone one of the Trimurti, to pay respect to one and all creatures equally, especially those which came into existence not from them and from beyond their capabilities. The Nava Kumaras are as much the children of Shiva as me or Ganesha. They deserve the same respect that is given to me or Ganesha.

'Further, Nandi was given respect by you and these brave warriors here are nothing less than Nandi in their ability, prowess or importance. Even if they were not, returning a salutation is basic etiquette. Someone as illustrious as yourself should know it.'

'I was diverted by my thoughts, my lord. After I paid my respects to Nandi, my mind was focused on how the queries to the supreme lord should be structured,' said Brahma, yet to salute the Nava Kumaras.

'You have four heads, Lord Brahma. They see in four directions. Even if one of them was left free to see where you are going and who you are crossing, you would not have failed to acknowledge me or them. Leave that aside, can I know what was so engaging that all four of your heads were so deep in thought that they were not aware of their surroundings?' asked Muruga.

'I was here to discuss with Mahadeva some aspects of creation that came up during my work. I needed some clarification on what the right approach was,' said Brahma.

'Can I know the specifics?' asked Muruga.

'You are but a mere child. You would not understand,' said Brahma. Veerabahu almost lost his temper but stayed back, not wanting to interrupt his lord.

'When an ignorant person or a student asks the learned, it is his duty to teach the person, even if it is beyond his capability to understand. The mark of a good teacher is to break things down so that even the lowest of beings can understand. You, Lord Brahma, are considered to be the first among teachers, for you have complete knowledge and understanding, which you have taught to the rishis, gurus and Devas. Kindly illuminate my knowledge as well,' requested Muruga.

Pushed into a corner, Brahma said, 'It is related to the Vedas, based on which I have performing my duty as preceptor. It is beyond the reach or understanding of a child.'

'First attempt to teach me, my lord, then, you can assess my capabilities. One can never realize how fast a horse can run unless one mounts it and rides it. Mount my mind, ride it and see how far and fast it can run,' said Muruga.

'The Vedas come from, commence with, and are encapsulated by the sound "Aum",' started Brahma, wanting to scare off the child without offending him.

'Perfect. Let us start with Aum. What is Aum?' asked Muruga.

'"Ah", "Uh" and "M" together form the sound Aum, with each of sound having its own significance, corresponding to cosmic creation stages. It is synonymous with Parabrahmam,' said Brahma.

'What is Parabrahmam?' asked Muruga.

'It is...' hesitated Brahma.

'It is?' prompted Muruga.

'I am not sure how to...' Brahma trailed off.

'Not sure how to or not sure what it is?' asked Muruga.

'I am not sure what it is,' conceded Brahma.

'You are the progenitor of the universe, tasked with regulating the creation process. You yourself acknowledged that the process is done in tune with the Vedas. You told me that the Vedas are an elaboration of Aum. You further said that Aum is synonymous with Parabrahmam but yet, you are not aware of what it is?

'If the progenitor himself is doing his task with half-baked knowledge, what would the products of the creation regulated by him be? If you were not aware, the moment you realized your ignorance, you should have approached those who knew and clarified it. Yet, you chose to continue with your work without understanding the importance or the true nature of your work.

'My father, Mahadeva, or my uncle, Mahavishnu, would have gladly sat with you and taught you everything all over again. It is merely your arrogance that you chose not to ask. Come here!' said Muruga.

Upon seeing Muruga and the Nava Kumaras who were willing to do as he said, Brahma went to him. Muruga then formed a fist and hit Brahma's forehead as punishment. That fist was felt on the heads of all the beings that traced their ancestry back to Brahma. Muruga then ordered the Nava Kumaras to arrest Brahma and keep him in solitary confinement until he understood and was ready and able to elaborate on the true nature of Parabrahmam to Muruga.

Ganesha saw this and came running.

Swaminatha

'No Muruga! This is wrong!' said Ganesha, seeing that his beloved brother would land in trouble.

'I am doing as prescribed by our father. The punishment I have given to Brahma is in line with the punishment prescribed by our father to those who forgot what they were taught and could not teach others what they had learned,' said Muruga.

'But Brahma is one of the Trimurti,' said Ganesha.

'Even if our father had made this mistake, the punishment would have been the same and I would have imprisoned him as well,' said Muruga calmly.

Parvati came in on hearing this and said, 'How dare you speak like that, Muruga? You are speaking to your brother about punishing your father, who is none other than Mahadeva himself.'

'Do not forget, my beloved mother, what Father had said. He said that all of us, being the subject of the multiverse, are not exempt from any of its laws or rules. We are to abide by them. If they are applicable to Mahadeva himself, why not to Brahmadeva?' asked Muruga.

'Even if it is applicable, it is the task of the elders to punish the elders. Besides, who will regulate the creation process if Brahma is in prison?' asked Parvati.

'I have already taken over the creation process. I can also do the preservation process as well as the destruction process, thanks to the blessings of my beloved father, the all-powerful Mahadeva. It is not about what one is capable of, Mother. If a mistake is made, the onus on righting the wrong is everyone's responsibility, irrespective of their age. This too has been decreed by Mahadeva.

'Further, when your erstwhile father, Daksha, made the mistake of not inviting Mahadeva to the yagna, it was you, her daughter, someone far younger than him, who went to stop him and later punish him,' said Muruga. Parvati had no counter argument. Further, she realized that her son was no longer the sweet child Guha who implicitly obeyed whatever he was told, but was Muruga, the enlightened god of victory, who spoke about events that had happened eons ago as if he had been there.

Upon hearing what happened from Nandi, Mahadeva came out. Everyone fell silent. Ganesha was worried about his brother getting punished. Seeing Mahadeva, Muruga saluted him and responded.

'I would like to explain what happened, Father,' started Muruga.

'I know what happened,' said Mahadeva. 'Release Brahma now,

and that is my order as your father. Someone who knows all that is there should also know that the father's order is to be obeyed verbatim.'

Muruga did as he was told.

'Come with me,' said Mahadeva. Ganesha tried to intervene, but Mahadeva refused.

'It was my fault. Please do not punish Muruga. He was in the right in everything that happened. Thanks to him, in my time in prison, I meditated and recollected your discourse,' said Brahma.

'I apologize, nonetheless, for your treatment, Lord Brahma. Kindly proceed with your work,' said Mahadeva as he took Muruga into his cavern.

'I told Muruga not to interfere. I am afraid for him now. He just came back. I do not want to be away from him,' said Ganesha.

'Do not worry. Your father is not a tyrant. Muruga is not a child either. All this is happening for a reason,' said Parvati.

Once inside, Mahadeva heard the arguments of Muruga again and at the point where he punished Brahma, Mahadeva stopped him.

'Did you know that the punishment for forgetting a lesson can be administered only by someone who can and will be able to explain the lesson in a proper manner?' asked Mahadeva.

'Yes, Father,' said Muruga.

'Then tell me the meaning of Aum, the Vedas and the true nature of Parabrahmam,' said Mahadeva.

'Kindly get off the high seat, Father, for it is the teacher's chair. The person teaching is to sit there while the student is seated lower,' said Muruga.

'I am your father,' said Mahadeva.

'I am your teacher now,' said Muruga.

'I already know the lesson you are teaching me,' said Mahadeva.

'Then this will be the recollection. You will still be the student and I will still be the teacher,' said Muruga.

Mahadeva conceded and took a lower seat, kneeling down while

Muruga sat on the chair. Muruga then went on to elaborate on the meaning of Aum, the true nature of Parabrahmam and the Vedas, while Mahadeva, like a dutiful student and a proud father, kneeled down and relearnt everything he knew from his son. At the end of the discourse, Mahadeva got up, hugged Muruga and proudly said, 'Your interpretation of the sacred knowledge is beautiful. I am proud as a father today.'

Both came out with enlightened faces, having discoursed on the divine knowledge. Mahadeva then turned to Muruga and said, 'Subrahmanya! ("Su" means to distil, "Brahman" means the divine knowledge, "Ya" means to do the act, referring to someone who distilled the divine knowledge and gave it.) Swaminatha! ("Swami" referring to Mahadeva and "Natha" meaning master, making Muruga the master of Mahadeva, as in his teacher.) Visit the Asura empire one last time and gather whatever knowledge Agastya has collected, based on his extensive and intrusive travels. The time is near. This is your war. You will have to plan it and play it fair and according to the rules. Your strategic ability as a warrior and general should speak more than your powers as my son.'

Vishnu, in his Yoganidra, saw and heard the entire scene and a couple of tears rolled down his cheeks, tears of joy at hearing the new and beautiful interpretation of the Vedas, Aum and Parabrahmam in the sweet voice of his son-in-law, Muruga.

Devayani

From the two tear drops of Vishnu emerged two beautiful young girls. They bowed to Vishnu, who blessed them and said, 'You were the result of Skanda's discourse on Parabrahmam. Seek his feet, seek his hand, for you belong to him. Go to Sara Vana, perform penance for him.'

They two went to what was left of Sara Vana and started their penance. One of them, without any patience, went on to sacrifice her life, engaged in endless continuous penance in her quest to please her lord, while the other engaged in regular prayer, displayed as Bhakti.

Soon, Muruga appeared before them. Their eyes swelled with tears of joy at the sight of their lord. They were rendered speechless. Muruga, being the kindest of the gods and the sole purpose of their existence, they got to witness their beloved lord sooner than many.

Muruga said, 'I know who you are. I know your purpose for doing this penance. I am here to grant you the boons your hearts truly desire, but I came into being for a specific purpose and I cannot marry anyone until this purpose is fulfilled.'

He turned to the girl who was in constant penance and said, 'Until then, you will go to Indra. He will adopt you and name you. Once the time comes, I will come and claim you for my wife.'

He then turned to the other girl and said, 'You will go to the Asura empire. You will be adopted by Nambiraja, the king of a mountain tribe. He is my ardent devotee as well and wants a girl child. When the time comes, I will claim you for my bride as well. Both of you will forget your origins and this event until then.'

They obeyed him and did as they were told. The sister who went towards Kailash as instructed by Muruga reached the outskirts of Sara Vana. A Rakshasa saw her and wanted her immediately. He started to chase her. Indra was in the vicinity; he heard the loud cry of the girl and ran to check. Seeing the Rakshasa chasing a very young girl child, Indra defeated the Rakshasa and saved the girl.

'Who are you, my child? Why was the Rakshasa chasing you? You need not be afraid of anything now. I will save you from any danger you might be in,' said he to her.

The girl replied, 'O mighty sir! I am an orphan. I do not know of my origins. The Rakshasa wanted to marry me. I will marry only the one who defeats the Devas and the Asuras and no one else. I will marry the one who never loses his temper at me.'

'I am Indra, the ruler of the universe,' replied Indra, amused by her answer. 'I will take you as my daughter if you are willing. I will name you Devayani and find you a groom who can not only defeat my sworn enemy the Asuras but also myself,' said Indra, laughing at her naivety and worried about her future. 'It is not safe now and things are going to get worse. Come with me, my child,' said Indra kindly.

The girl followed Indra to his abode in Kailash, far away and safe from the clutches of the Asura empire. Indra performed a simple ritual under the guidance of Narada to adopt Devayani and make her his daughter.

Meanwhile, deep inside the Asura empire, over the mountains, Nambiraja had gone hunting. Much like Parvati was found by Himavat and Mainavati, he found a girl among the creepers and name her Valli.

Valli, adopted by a family that was deeply entrenched in the worship of Cheyyon, propagated there by Agastya and Avvai, became enamoured and deeply devoted to Muruga, so much so that all her being was consumed by him and him alone. She became the cherished princess of the clan, a warrior princess. She was fully capable of defending the forest and protecting the animals from poachers. She also took care of the people's farms.

While Valli was completely devoted to her family as well as to her personal deity Muruga, Devayani grew up as the daughter of Indra. She was as obedient a daughter as a father could ever ask for. She took care of his needs while he was in hiding. She trusted him blindly and believed that he would give to her what she had as her only request, a husband who would never lose his temper while being a ferocious and powerful warrior who can beat both Devas and Asuras, with her father being the king of Devas.

Meanwhile, as Mahadeva had ordered, Muruga ventured into the Asura empire. He met Agastya, who gave him valuable inputs that would help him plan and strategize his attack on the Asura empire. He had different plans for his meeting with Avvai, who had learnt about who Muruga was from Agastya. Muruga initially toyed with her, then had a debate in Tamil and finally blessed her. He also asked her to aid his forces when the time came.

Shaktivel

*M*uruga came back to Kailash. On his return, Mahadeva called him, Parvati, Ganesha, the Nava Kumaras and Nandi, along with Brahma, Indra, Narada, Agni and Yama.

His eyes opened slowly, and he said, 'The time is now. Muruga, for this mission, take over command of the Ganas from Ganesha. Nandi will also give you the Ganas he has for securing and maintaining Kailash. Indra! Make him the general of your army and give him official command. Every single Deva, no matter who he is, if they were ever under your dominion, their loyalty should be extended to him. They should follow his every command. Lord Brahma will conduct the ceremony.

'You have all my blessings. You are created for victory. There is no failure in your existence. No matter what the odds, if you step in, victory is sure. His boon states that his death can come only through me and from my Shakti. You came from my Shakti. Go forth and remove the entire Asura clan from the face of the multiverse. Take your mother's blessings and leave for battle.'

Mahadeva went back to his meditative state as they all left.

Ganesha called his chief Gana as did Nandi. Both ordered their forces to follow Muruga's command. Meanwhile, Brahma and Narada commenced the ritual for Muruga to receive his commission from Indra. Muruga, having taken command of the Ganas from Ganesha, requested his blessings, worshipping him first before starting the task. He also sought Nandi's blessings, who offered them wholeheartedly. Muruga then went to meet his mother in her quarters.

She was waiting patiently, joyous to see her beloved son being crowned. He came to her, saw and experienced the joy in her and then prostrated himself at her feet. She stood at the centre of her cavern, closed her eyes and went into a meditative stance, focusing all her mind and energy on her roots, Adi Shakti. The cavern began to heat up as she connected to her roots. She split herself into two, taking out the connected energy in her own form. The form glowed, the purest form of infinite energy. Muruga worshipped the form as Parvati solidified it into a divine spear, Shaktivel. She handed it over to Muruga. The Vel was Muruga's choice of weapon and the one he was adept at using. This Vel, however, was the purest form of energy, sourced directly from Parvati's connection with Adi Shakti. When required, this Vel was capable of directing as much energy as required to complete a task, from the eternal infinite root source of all energy.

'Muruga! This Vel is me and I am this Vel. Give it a task and cast it. It will not return to you without accomplishing the task it is assigned, no matter how difficult or complex it may seem. This Vel is my Shakti and thereby it is Shaktivel. It is full of divine wisdom and, therefore, Jnana Vel (Wisdom Vel). It is devoid of failure and, hence, Vetri Vel (Victory Vel). This Vel is fearless and, hence, Veera Vel (Bravery Vel),' said Parvati.

She then called the Nava Kumaras and said, 'Go with him, be his shadow. May his will be your way.'

As soon as Muruga stepped out, before him were the Ganas, Indra, Vayu, Agni and Yama, while Brahma and Narada stood by his side. Muruga spoke, 'I appoint the Nava Kumaras my commanders and Veerabahu will be the commander-in-chief.'

He then turned to Veerabahu and said, 'Divide the Ganas into six theatres and assign them to your generals, except for

Veerakesari and Veeramartanda. The two of them, for now, will be your assignees. I have a specific task for them, which I will let you know when the time comes.'

'I request your permission to speak,' said Veerabahu.

'Neither you, nor your commanders require permission to speak with me. I appoint you nine as my inner council. Feel free to give your opinions and thoughts,' Muruga responded. He then turned to the Ganas and said, 'Any word coming out of their mouth is an order from me. Obey it and victory shall be ours.'

Veerabahu turned to Indra and said, 'I would like to know the reward my general will receive upon successfully completing the mission.' Muruga smiled.

'I will give up the post of ruler of the multiverse to Muruga upon his completing his commission,' said Indra.

Veerabahu laughed and replied, 'He is beyond all posts. He is fully capable of taking over the multiverse for himself, if he chooses to.'

'I will give my daughter, Devayani, to Muruga as his wife, making him my son-in-law,' said Indra.

'That would be the perfect gift, Devayani as his second wife, for his first wife forever shall be the goddess of victory. On behalf of my general, we accept,' said Veerabahu.

'Vetri Vel!' shouted Veerabahu. The brothers responded, 'Veera Vel!' He repeated the chant a second time and this time, the Ganas joined in as well. Then, for the final time, Veerabahu shouted using all his might, 'Vetri Vel!' and the Ganas along with the Nava Kumaras, Indra, Vayu, Agni and Yama joined him and shouted feverishly, 'Veera Vel!'

Yuddha Parva

Vatapi

*V*atapi and Ilvala were living as hermits in disguise, but were far from being actual hermits. They, true to their mother's nature and order, continued to act as hermits while reeling in unsuspecting rishis to their ashram.

Once a victim was in, Ilvala would ask Vatapi to become a fruit depending upon the season, which would be given to the innocent rishi as an offering. Once the rishi consumed the fruit, Ilvala revealed his true form, that of an Asura, and according to the boon given by Brahma, called his brother to come out.

The brother, who was in the stomach of the rishi, would tear out from inside, killing the person. They enjoyed the painful screams of their victims and more than the meat they consumed. Once they realized that this did not work with the Devas, rishis became their sole focus. The Devas, who managed to become fugitives, were caught by them and handed over to the Asura army.

Agastya was wandering the lands, performing his deeds according to the orders of Mahadeva. He came to this particular forest upon the order of Muruga, who told Agastya that he would be the cause of the unnatural death of an Asura from the first family, which would signal the beginning of the end.

Once Agastya entered the forest, information reached Ilvala, who wanted to kill Agastya, more as a trophy kill than anything else. Ilvala and Vatapi knew that he was not immortal and if he fell for their trick, they would win the respect of the Asuras for killing someone so powerful.

As Agastya went about his daily ablutions, Ilvala arrived, disguised as a sage.

'Salutations, O holy one!' said Ilvala, who had already asked his brother to turn into a fruit and wait under a tree, just to be sure that Agastya's suspicions are not aroused. Agastya completed his ablutions and returned the salutations.

'I am Vallaba. I am a sage from these parts. I serve those who serve Lord Mahadeva and through my service, I hope to attain the grace of the supreme lord,' said Ilvala.

'What a great service you render! You are indeed a blessed soul. I am so fortunate to have met you today. I am hungry and there is no house or ashram around where I can get some food,' said Agastya. He was aware of the tale that was going around the nearby villages, that sages who go into the forest never come out.

'Indeed, I am the blessed one to be able to host a sage who meditates on Mahadeva day and night. Please come to my ashram and I shall serve you well,' said Ilvala.

'Let us go then, O holy Vallaba,' said Agastya. They walked towards the ashram that had been built by Ilvala. As they crossed a tree, Ilvala stopped, seeing his brother under the tree as a fruit. As soon as he stopped, before he opened his mouth, Agastya said, 'See there! There is a ripe fruit that has fallen off by itself. Being a sage, we are only allowed to consume such a fruit. This is going to be a good day, for I take this as an auspicious sign.'

Ilvala was first confused and then elated that fortune was on his side. Agastya was walking to his grave by himself, allowing Ilvala to take the credit.

'Yes, O peerless seer. This is an auspicious sign. I will get the fruit,' said Ilvala. They arrived at the ashram, where Agastya was given a seat. Ilvala took the fruit, placed it on a leaf without washing either and placed it before Agastya.

'Kindly cut the fruit, O noble Vallaba, and take out the seed,' said Agastya.

This threw Ilvala off. Cutting the fruit meant hurting his brother, Vatapi. Ilvala quickly regrouped and said, 'O seer, this fruit is meant to be consumed whole. The tree is a holy one and the fruit is known to give the person who consumes it a very long life, but only if it is consumed whole.'

Agastya understood what was happening. He had been sent by Muruga to be the first to kill an Asura. The villagers narrated stories where no rishi who entered the forest ever came out alive. He was interrupted by a sage during his ablutions, something out of the ordinary. The ashram did not follow the scriptures that prescribed how an ashram should be built. They found a fruit with no corresponding broken end in the tree, not to mention that riper fruits are yet to fall off the tree. Agastya's feet were neither washed nor was he asked to wash them himself. When asked to cut the fruit, the sage in front of him was alarmed. Agastya realized that this fruit was designed to kill him from the inside in one manner or another.

Considering that it was not meant to be cut, he also surmised that this fruit was a part of an Asura or an Asura, where cutting the fruit would harm the said Asura. He invoked the power granted by Mahadeva, similar to the one granted by Muruga to Avvai, the power that makes his word come true. He swallowed the fruit as a whole and said, 'Jeernothbava.' The phrase meant to be completely digested. True to his word, the fruit and the Asura were completely digested inside Agastya's stomach.

Ilvala laughed out loudly, while still in the guise of Vallaba.

'What happened, O seer?' asked Agastya.

'There is no jeernothbava yet. Once we kill you and consume you, then there will be jeernothbava,' said Ilvala.

'But sir, you are a sage who serves those who serve god. How can you consume meat, let alone that of a human, and that too of a sage and, on top of that, of a sage who meditates on the divine lord himself?' asked Agastya.

Ilvala laughed louder saying, 'I am no sage. I am an Asura. I am a royal Asura. I am the son of Ajamukhi, the nephew of Surapadma, the emperor of the multiverse. I am also a half rishi, being the son of Durvasa. My mission is to hurt and kill as many rishis as possible, as ordered by mother. You, Sage Agastya, will be the crown jewel among my victims. My respect will increase multi-fold once the Asuras know that I have killed you.'

'You may be an Asura, and a royal one at that, but you are no rishi. Being the son of rishi does not make one so. To become a rishi, discipline and devotion are essential. You have neither. Further, you do not have the power to kill me,' said Agastya.

'You fool! You are already dead. You just do not know it yet. The fruit you consumed is my brother, Vatapi. Once I summon him, he will tear you from the inside, killing you. We have been granted the boon by the grand preceptor, Brahma himself. Vatapi, come out!' said Ilvala.

There was complete silence.

'Vatapi! I, your elder brother, order you to come out!' said Ilvala. Again, there was no response.

'Vatapi! What is happening? Can't you hear me?' demanded Ilvala.

'He can't hear you. He is no more. He has been digested,' said Agastya.

'You trickster! Evil being! You killed my sibling. You will pay for it with your life,' said Ilvala, as he pounced on the sage.

Agastya simply moved aside and threw his Danda (the Y-shaped staff that sages use to place their arms on and meditate), which he used to rest his arms during meditation. The Danda turned into a monstrous python and swallowed the evil Ilvala whole, digesting him to his end.

The first two Asuras belonging to the family that had enslaved the multiverse were thus killed. Ajamukhi felt her children's death and howled in anguish, hearing which Tarakasura, in whose palace she was residing, came running to her.

Mayapuri

 $\mathcal{A}$ s soon as Tarakasura understood what had happened from Ajamukhi and later his informers, he summoned Mahadheera, his general, and ordered him to go along with his most capable warriors towards the area locked between the three kingdoms and kill the sage. He realized that the sage was powerful enough to have restored balance to the land during Mahadeva's marriage. Tarakasura feared that Agastya had been quietly bringing in a cultural change, preparing the subjects in his kingdom for a change of guard either through their tacit support or active participation in a rebellion.

Meanwhile, Muruga, along with his massive Gana army and powerful generals, marched towards Mayapuri. Muruga was in a massive chariot that belonged to Mahavishnu himself, who had gifted the same to his son-in-law for the war. It was pulled by the best of horses and was helmed by Vayu, who was known for his adept charioting skills.

Once they crossed the Vindhyas, they could see the beautiful city in all its glorious splendour, backed by the Krauncha mountain. Muruga ordered them to camp there and summoned his nine generals to strategize for the attack.

'Veerabahu, we are going to attack from the same front twice. Right now, Agastya would have done as I had ordered, taking attention away from us. Now is the right time to attack. We are not going to negotiate or take hostages. Do not hurt women or children. The rest have to die. Spare none. Tarakasura has neither respect nor devotion for Mahadeva and therefore deserves no mercy. Furthermore, he is bound to see us as inferior, for our might is yet to be proven, while his is established as something capable of bringing a stalemate with Mahavishnu himself.

'Anyone who sees his enemy as his inferior and underestimates him is bound to lose. This is applicable to gods as well. Indra's underestimation of the Asuras led to his downfall. Tarakasura's underestimation of us will lead to his downfall. Only after we destroy Mayapuri and kill Tarakasura will our might be respected by Surapadma and we will be given a chance to negotiate. Take three of the six units under your brothers with you. Take Veerakesari as well and make him your second in command for your front. Burn this city down, for that is the order of Mahadeva. Fight valiantly. Free the Devas first, arm them and enrol them under Veerakesari. He will be the general for the Deva division of our army.

'I will come in once their hand rises as his reinforcements are bound to kick in sooner than later. Our attack should be the first and it should be the last; for Tarakasura and Mayapuri, it will be the final and fatal one as well. Remember the formations that I am about to give to you for this front,' said Muruga as began to elaborate the same to them.

The Nava Kumaras listened intently and hung on to his every word. Once they had their orders, Veerabahu, along with Veerakesari and three of his brothers as well as their theatre, marched towards Mayapuri.

Needless to say, the signs of complete destruction started to haunt the magnificent city. Vultures started to circle around the palace. Water blackened. The sky became cloudy. The rain turned red. Lightning struck, and the resultant thunder sounded like a donkey braying. Women had nightmares where they saw themselves as widows or their husbands without their heads. Children cried inconsolably from fear. This was a new feeling for the entire city, since the time it came into existence. Jackals, hyenas and wolves ran from the jungle into the city.

Tarakasura felt that something was not right and immediately sent off his sister, Ajamukhi, to Veeramahendrapuri. His wives refused to leave while his children stood by him.

Soon, one division of Muruga's army, led by Veerakesari, under Veerandhaka, entered the fort in wedge formation. The guards were no match for the sons of Shiva who entered the palace in full swing, shouting, 'Vetri Vel! Veera Vel!' Like the head of a spear tearing through flesh, they broke in through the first line of defence. As powerful as Tarakasura's army was, they were untested for the lack of better opponents and it showed in their fighting.

Before Tarakasura could react, the second division under Veerapuruhuta entered in herringbone formation. Once inside, they fanned out in all directions. The Asuras were surprised and confounded. The formation broke to reveal another herringbone formation led by Veeramaheswara and his division. Seeing the number of the enemies multiply by the minute left the Asura army desperate and they started to scatter.

Veerakesari, meanwhile, went straight for the prison, based on inputs by spies, freed the Devas and armed them with Asura armoury.

Without Mahadheera at his cue, Tarakasura and his son, Asurendran came out to battle right away. Tarakasura went after Veerakesari, seeing this more as an attempt to free Devas rather than an attack on his empire. Asurendran went after Veerapuruhuta. However, upon seeing the second herringbone formation, he was stuck by fear, for he wondered how many more such formations were inside and where these warriors were springing from.

Seeing his able men run, he thought it was best to fetch Mahadheera and summon him along with the unparalleled warriors who had gone with him. He quickly left the war scene towards Krauncha to bring back his best men. The Asura soldiers, upon seeing their leader desert them, started to scatter and were slaughtered by Muruga's army.

Veerakesari and Tarakasura were meanwhile fighting all out. Tarakasura simply brushed off the arrows that came towards him, and, taking on his true form, that of an elephant-headed giant, rampaged through Muruga's army. He then took a powerful Astra and aimed for Veerakesari's heart. Upon the Astra striking him, he fainted, unable to bear the pain.

The tables were now turned and upon seeing their general lose consciousness, the Devas were struck with dread. They quickly picked up Veerakesari's chariot and made a rush for the empire gates. Veerandhaka quickly engulfed Veerakesari and had him escorted to the base camp, picking up where Veerakesari had left.

Unfortunately, he too was no match for the vile Asura. He fought long and hard, but the same arrow that felled his brother also felled him. His orders for his division were different though. His division, which comprised of Agni's army led by Jwala, were more focussed on setting the city on fire after throwing out the women and children, leaving the Asura soldiers busy in their attempts to put out the fire. Jwala followed her orders diligently, making sure the women and children were safe and at the same time, the city was being destroyed. She made good on her mission.

Tarakasura had chased Veerandhaka outside while he was being escorted, where he faced one more herringbone which was tearing the Asura army apart. He took an even more powerful gigantic elephant form and banged his foot hard on the earth. This immediately caused the earth to crack and the crack ran towards the formation. Veerapuruhuta quickly ordered his men to spread out to save themselves, which they did. As they all left, in the centre of the final herringbone was Veerabahu. He too stamped his feet, which sent a similar shockwave that blocked Tarakasura's wave, shocking him.

'Who are you!' he thundered.

'I am Veerabahu, son of Mahadeva, general of Skanda, Shiva's incarnate, who is also the general of the Devas commissioned to end your race. Surrender now and he might spare your life,' came the reply from Veerabahu.

'You fool! Don't you know who I am? I am Tarakasura. The one who Mahavishnu himself could not defeat. No power can defeat me.' As soon as he finished the sentence, he was struck by an ordinary arrow that made him fall down. This was the second time he fell down in his entire existence; the first time had been when Mahavishnu had struck him.

'Surrendering is not in your destiny, death is. Are you going to talk or fight?' asked Veerabahu.

They both rained immensely powerful arrows at each other. Veerabahu had a counter for every single arrow that was fired at him. He kept him engaged for long enough for Jwala, Veeramaheswara and Veerapuruhuta to do their work. The Devas, seeing Veerabahu stand up to Tarakasura, jumped in full-fledged and the Asuras were outnumbered, outmatched and outpowered. They were unable to match the prowess of Jwala, Veeramaheswara or Veerapuruhuta.

Tarakasura paused for a moment and looked around him. His beautiful city, his palace, his kingdom was engulfed in flames that rose to the skies. His warriors were running for their lives at the sight of the Devas and Ganas. Those who weren't running were dead. His son was nowhere to be found. Enraged, Tarakasura recollected that he had built all this from nothing and was never dependent on anyone else to save him. He channelled all his rage into the war and started showering arrows in all directions as well as at Veerabahu.

He aimed the Agneyastra, the weapon from Agni that would burn everything in its path, at the army of Muruga, who were laying his city to waste. They were shaken at the sight. Jwala, seeing the effect, shot back a Mahagneyastra, a new Astra designed by herself, who foresaw this eventuality. This countered the Agneyastra, reducing it to ashes.

Veerabahu and Tarakasura then increased their attacks on each other with Varunastra, Suryastra and even Narayanastra. Veerabahu countered them in a similar manner, rendering them completely useless. At his wits end, Tarakasura began to trample the army, indiscriminately killing the soldiers. Seeing this, Veerabahu took out a new Astra, Veerabhadrastra. This was the one that contained the entire power that Veerabhadra, who destroyed Daksha's yagna, possessed.

'Tarakasura, your death is to occur by Mahadeva's Shakti and his Shakti alone. This is the Veerabhadrastra. This is Mahadeva's Shakti. Your end is nigh,' said Veerabahu, as he shot the same towards Tarakasura.

Tarakasura realized that Veerabahu was not bluffing, for the Astra was approaching him fast, spitting cosmic fire. He quickly disappeared from the battleground, using the Maya taught by his mother. He still had hope for a second front with his general returning. If he could get his enemies to Krauncha, he could win the battle and the war with him, Krauncha and Mahadheera fighting as one.

With him gone, the rest of the Asuras were sitting ducks. They were killed and Mayapuri was burned down in a couple of hours. The Devas left and the army of Agni led by Jwala were quick to act, using the opportunity to completely ransack whatever was left of the Asura army in the once-beautiful and magnificent city of Mayapuri, bringing to fruition the curse of Durvasa.

Krauncha

*V*eerabahu, however, had already been apprised by Muruga of who Krauncha was and his close friendship with Tarakasura. He knew that Tarakasura would run to Krauncha. Veerabahu quickly installed Jwala as the queen regent of Mayapuri as instructed by Muruga, left behind the injured Devas along with Jwala's division from Agni, leaving her in charge as he stormed towards Krauncha with his brothers, their Ganas and the rest of the Devas.

Asurendran also came back with reinforcements and Tarakasura's able general, who had gone to get Agastya. Tarakasura felt like he was back in control when he saw them and Krauncha. He still had hope. He still had a place.

Mahadheera, like Krauncha, was almost a brother who had stood by Tarakasura in all his battles, including that with Vishnu. He had risked his life, almost sacrificing himself by throwing himself in harm's way to save his king during his battle with Vishnu. If his loyalty was great, his ferocity was nothing less. In the battlefield, he was like Tarakasura when it came to prowess and power.

Tarakasura's enemies, if and when some dumb minor king in the multiverse chose to rebel, dreaded the mere mention of Mahadheera. The general even refused to have his own kingship, for it would take his attention away from performing his duty to Tarakasura, which he valued more. Tarakasura had greater respect for Mahadheera, as a matter of fact, than for his son, who could not live up to the might and power of the previous generation. This was precisely the reason he picked him and his best division to handle the Agastya menace, who quietly was preparing his subjects for rebellion. Agastya was, after all, someone who had restored the balance of the universe when all the gods had assembled for Mahadeva's wedding and was someone who killed his powerful nephews. Someone with that much power and stature required someone like Mahadheera.

Krauncha, who had a single consciousness with the mountain itself and controlled it by his mere thought, said that he would take care of Veerabahu.

Veerabahu, leading from front, believed that he was chasing Tarakasura but it was an illusion created by the Asura. The illusion entered a cave in the mountain. Muruga had warned him of the treacherous nature of the mountain but Veerabahu, in his zeal to finish off Tarakasura, ran into the cave. The mountain closed itself, trapping Veerabahu within itself.

The other brothers, Veerapuruhuta and Veeramaheswara, along with their divisions, which now included the Devas, came after him, but were left outside Krauncha with no idea where Veerabahu had gone.

Krauncha allowed Veerabahu's voice to reach outside, as Veerabahu yelled to find a way out. Then, it muted Veerabahu's voice and mimicked him instead, as if he were desperate and dying, thereby breaking the morale of the army. Veerabahu meanwhile sat down and started praying to Muruga to find a way out of the place.

Asurendran, Tarakasura and Mahadheera covered the army from the rear. With Veerabahu trapped and dying inside a cave and with certain destruction standing behind and ahead of them, the army was confused and afraid. They all realized that they were trapped. Veeramaheswara and Veerapuruhuta then yelled, 'Vetri Vel!' and hearing the chant, the army was motivated to fight till death and die as warriors rather than cowards.

Tarakasura and Asurendran laughed loudly, while the former said, 'No amount of motivation can save you now. Your Vetri Vel and Veera Vel are useless. Let this be a lesson to anyone who ever thinks of even lifting their eye to face an Asura! Your death will be immortalized as a tale to strike fear in the hearts of those who dare to take on an Asura. You have come much farther than any of our enemies, destroying my beautiful Mayapuri. You will pay for it dearly.'

'There is no death for those who have surrendered completely to our lord Muruga. He will save us!' said Veeramaheswara.

'Let us see if your little boy will come. Who knows? He may already have run away, seeing that his army is trapped and is going to die,' said Asurendran.

'I hope your Muruga comes here so that we can send out a clear message. No son of Mahadeva, not even Mahadeva himself can now stand up to the might of the Asura empire!' said Mahadheera.

No sooner than he uttered the words, a spear, shining so brightly that it blurred the vision of the entire Asura army, tore through the wind, going at such a high speed that it rendered those in the vicinity deaf. It passed between Asurendran and Tarakasura, taking their massive general's head off his body, right into the Krauncha mountain. The mountain exploded, killing Krauncha the demon as well as the mountain. Tarakasura realized that he was not the hunter but the hunted; he was the one who had actually walked into the trap set by the little boy. In a single stroke, the little boy had destroyed the confidence that Tarakasura had gained, thanks to the support of his dear friend Krauncha and his peerless general.

Veerabahu came out valiantly saying, 'Vetri Vel!' and the whole army chorused after him. The Asura army, which now had the best of warriors left, fought valiantly. Their leaders and commanders fell one by one to the onslaught of the Nava Kumaras. Veerabahu went after Asurendran while the other brothers including Veerakesari and Veerandhaka came from behind and took on mighty Asura warriors. Tarakasura tried to step in between Veerabahu and his son, Asurendran.

Veerabahu simply pointed him backwards, saying, 'Being the highest among the Asuras here, your death now will be at the hands of the highest among our army, our lord, Skanda!' Asurendran and Veerabahu started to fight hard but for the man who almost killed Tarakasura, Asurendran was no match. He started to retreat and run. Veerabahu deemed it unnecessary to chase after him, for he never was or would be a threat and joined the brothers in ransacking what was left of the Asura army.

Tarakasura turned back and the sight before him was breathtaking. A handsome young man with broad shoulders and a glowing face was seated on a magnificent chariot helmed by Vayu, with horses provided by the Ashwins, and a Vel in his hand. He had a third eye in each of his six heads and twelve arms, with ten of them wielding a variety of weapons. Tarakasura realized that his last moments were near. The sight of the boy filled his heart with untold bliss, the kind of bliss that he had never experienced. He felt as if Mahadeva had himself come disguised as a boy. He wanted to prostrate before Muruga, but he controlled himself.

'Muruga! You are the son of Shiva, I can tell. Our Asura clan received the boon from Shiva that we cannot be killed by anyone except by his power. We have no enmity towards Mahadeva. What we are doing to the Devas is none of your business. I will still give you a chance. Leave now or else you will die,' said Tarakasura.

Muruga smiled and said, 'Taraka! Your words belie your thoughts. It is true that Maheswara gave you the boons that elevated you to the stature of fighting Mahavishnu to a stalemate. Yet, you squandered all the gifts you received for meagre materialistic ends and cheap vengeance. You could have become a protector of the multiverse, could have ruled it wisely, could have made it a better place. Yet, you chose to focus selfishly on taking vengeance on the Devas. Mahadeva gave the boons as a reward for your penance and not your character. What I am about to give you, death, would be the reward for your character, which is responsible for your vile actions.'

Tarakasura, in his final attempt, took out the Pasupatastra. If he was going to die, he would not go alone and would take every single being around him. Everyone and everything that mattered to him were destroyed already. In all directions that he could see, there was death. Vultures were feasting off Asura bodies. Hyenas were laughing at him. Foxes and wolves were having a tough time choosing which ones to eat and which ones to leave. His kingdom was on fire and ravaged. There was nothing left.

He shot the Pasupatastra at Muruga. Seeing the Astra, everyone except Veerabahu were shaken. Veerabahu had unshakeable faith in his lord and brother, Muruga.

The Astra went straight towards Muruga's heart. It touched and pierced his armour. It touched his chest. It entered his chest. It disappeared. There was not even a scar on his chest. Muruga had absorbed his father's most beloved and most powerful Astra. Tarakasura's jaw dropped. He then tore the Sudarshan Chakra off his chest and threw it at him. Muruga caught it in his index finger and held it, as Mahavishnu would.

Muruga's army celebrated. Tarakasura was now all alone in the battlefield. His son too had run away like a weasel. Every single Asura was dead. He took his most ferocious form, of a giant elephant with eight tusks, and ran towards Muruga. Muruga took his Vel, and threw it, aiming for his forehead. The Vel whizzed right through to him, entered his forehead, went through his skull and pierced his brain, coming out on the other side before returning to its rightful owner, Muruga.

Tarakasura fell dead.

'Vetri Vel!' shouted Veerabahu.

'Veera Vel!' shouted the entire army. Their voice echoed across Mayapuri, where other voices also joined in the chant and their jubilant celebrations began with the first of the three kingdoms having fallen, freeing one third of the multiverse under Asura dominion.

Muruga ordered that the brave Asura be given a funeral befit of a fearless warrior. His wife, who loved him to death, entered the pyre, not wanting to live without him, despite Jwala's assurance that no harm would come to her and she would be treated as befits a queen.

Plan

*M*uruga quickly regrouped with his inner council and said, 'We have established ourselves as a threat now to Sura and his clan. We did not have much trouble in handling Tarakasura, for there was no reason for us to hold back. One, we were unestablished, leaving us little room for negotiation; we therefore had no choice. Two, he was no longer devoted to our father and we had no reason to show him mercy or give him a chance. Three, we had the surprise factor on our side. Four, we had Agastya's help to divert attention from us, which led to Mahadheera going away at the time of our first strike. We no longer enjoy all those advantages. Do you agree?'

Veerabahu replied, 'Yes, my lord. But we still have Mahadeva's blessings. There is no reason for us to hold back.'

Veerakesari said, 'Let us go for Asurapuri next and burn it to the ground. Finally, Veeramahendrapuri will fall too.'

Veeradheera said, 'With the might granted to us by our divine father and your divine mother, there should be no challenge and we should be done with all this in a day or two. The Devas and the others have suffered long enough.'

Veerandhaka and Veeramartanda too agreed, and with the rest of the brothers eagerly waited for Muruga to give them the word.

'No, Veeras. Remember what Father said. We are here on a war. We should fight the war as a general, soldier and commander, not as sons of Shiva. If Mahadeva wanted to destroy the three kingdoms, he would not require more than a single arrow or even a smile. He wanted us to re-establish Dharma through a fair fight. I know that one thought is troubling your mind.

'I could have gone for Tarakasura's head, but it would not have been fair. Even Mahadheera was killed in this manner because he abused the supreme lord, for which the punishment is immediate, and he was on the trajectory to the spot where Krauncha's heart resided. Besides, once in the battlefield in the middle of a war, a warrior should be open to attack from all sides and alert to any coming danger. Being the general, he should have known this.

'We will fight this war fairly. Both Surapadma and Simhamukha are staunch devotees of my father and my mother. There is the slightest chance that they can reform, and we need to give it to them. Simhamukha especially is probably the greatest among the devotees of my mother in her Kali form. He is also the kindest of the brothers. If we go for and get Surapadma to reform or perish,

Simhamukha would not want a war that would cause the mass destruction of his race.

'Our next target is Veeramahendrapuri. I have chosen Chendur as our base camp, from where we will commence operations. I want Veerakesari, Veerarakshasa, Veeradheera and Veeramartanda to march towards Chendur, clearing the area of all Asuras they meet on the way, and setting the people free. Once the people are free, they will come under the dominion of Jwala. She is aware of her role, for we need someone strong, able, just, generous and kind to consolidate the gains. Avvai will help her with the affairs of the state for the time being, with her infinite wisdom. The division we have left behind, Agni's, and the recovering Devas will help her with the task.

'Having lost a division, Veerakesari, you shall take the willing and able Devas and organize them into your division. I want to give you time, which is why you will not come to Chendur directly with me. Take your time, prepare and come.

'Veeramartanda, your task will be to organize the Manushyas, Nagas, Danavas and those who are opposed to and are the victims of Asura tyranny. Be very careful. They may have dual motives. You are a cautious person and a good judge of character, which is why I set you aside for this task. Take as much time as you need. You will find your way directly to the battlefield at the right time, guided by Mahadeva's blessings, and Agastya's experience and wisdom. You will meet him in the next town, where I have asked him to wait, till he hears the news of our victory.

'Veerandhaka and Veerapuruhuta fought valiantly from the forefront and they as well as their divisions took maximum damage. Let them and their divisions recuperate in the journey to Chendur with me.

'Veerakesari, Veeradheera, Veeramartanda and Veerarakshasa can go and start planning the details of their task.

'Veerabahu, Veerandhaka, Veerapuruhuta, Veeramaheswara

and Veerakendra should prepare for our journey to Chendur,' said Muruga. They all bowed to him, took leave of him and went to prepare for their tasks immediately.

Chendur

*K*adu, near Chendur, was a dense forest very close to the seashore, the very sea that stood at the border of the seventh circle of defence of Veeramahendrapuri and housed all that Sura was proud of. The place got its name from its red soil. The forest was mostly covered in deciduous trees, including peepal and palm trees. It was, however, devoid of other major life forms due to fear of Rakshasas, who came every now and then when bored with their lack of work.

After a millennium of going unchallenged, the circles of defences were now in name only, except for the inner two. The Rakshasas who guarded the circles were long gone as a race, leaving a handful of survivors who merely lived as scavengers. With the unlimited and bountiful treasures that the kingdom had at its disposal, and dearth and famine for rivals, complacency was at its peak in the kingdom.

The situation had become so complacent that Surapadma's last battle was fought before he had set up the kingdom and Banugopan was the last Sura clan member to fight a battle with a minor uprising from the empire of the sun which he squashed in hours, living up to his name. Banugopan did not even go with a huge army and it was pretty much a one-sided affair.

At night, with Veeramahendrapuri full of life and lit up in constant celebration of Asura might, and Chendur forest completely in the dark due to its vegetation and zero population, no two places could have been more different. Muruga picked this place more for its proximity than for its cover. He did not need cover.

He, as a general, knew very well that Sura would not take him seriously enough. Unless Banugopan or someone Sura valued highly was defeated and killed in the battlefield, Sura would not get to the negotiation table. He, as a god, knew that he was here to end Sura's fate and that is where all this was leading to.

Once Muruga set foot in Chendur, the dark dense lifeless forest sprang to life. Birds started to come, especially peacocks. Fruits and flowers blossomed out of season in an otherwise sleepy forest. Animals which avoided the place because of the visiting Rakshasas and Asuras, felt safe and returned to their home. Muruga went to the shore. He set his eyes on the beautiful city that shone like a full moon in its glory.

He felt a little sorry for the Asuras when he realized that he was going to raze the whole thing to the ground. All the hard work that had been put in to build such a beautiful splendour: all the lives and families that have been built in and around such a wonderful palace, with a pillar that connected heaven to earth at the centre, proudly hoisting the valiant Asura's flag; all the hopes for the future among the young children playing joyously; all of it will be made one with nature because of their ruler being unjust and cruel to a section of the multiverse he was supposed to rule and guard without partiality.

That was the basic difference between the Devas and Asuras, for the Devas never sought to wipe out the Asuras as a race and merely wanted to establish themselves as superior to their stepbrothers. The Asuras, on the other hand, even though superior in their devotion to the supreme lord, superior in their bravery and courage, superior in their ability to wield and control Maya, were still driven by the mad desire to put an end to Devas and rishis, thereby becoming submerged in the same Maya they so adeptly wielded, which ultimately became the reason for their downfall more than once.

The Veera brothers who accompanied Muruga camped there. Once Muruga set foot in Chendur Kadu, Indra joined Muruga with whoever he could gather. Muruga asked them to rest well for a couple of nights, as the operations for the brutal war should commence only at the right time. Until then, on the seashore, Muruga made a linga and sat in meditation and contemplation in front of it, worshipping it wholeheartedly.

When he woke up from his meditation, he took his Vel and plunged it deep into the soil. Fresh crystal water sprang from the spot, not far from the sea, which was filled with the saltiest of waters. Muruga then took the sweet crystal water and performed ablutions to Mahadeva on his linga, seeking his clemency for the large-scale slaughter and destruction of Asuras, a lot of whom were among the most ardent devotees of Mahadeva. Veerabahu, who was always by his side, accompanied him.

Once Muruga completed his prayers, Veerabahu asked him why he had to do so, for he came here on the orders of Mahadeva himself. Muruga explained to Veerabahu that even though he was doing the task assigned to him by Mahadeva, the karma that came out of the task would still be his. There was always a choice with him to not take up the task.

Muruga cited the Kumaras, who were the first born of Brahma. They were tasked by their father to pursue aggressive population of the universe. Yet, they chose to take a different path, seeking infinite knowledge and salvation for themselves, instead of indulging themselves with Maya. It is for the karma they accumulated by not obeying their father that they were long denied divine knowledge, which eluded them until Mahadeva chose to give them the same, only after their karma expired.

'Even Mahadeva himself was not spared from karma,' said Muruga, going on to tell Veerabahu the tale of Mahadeva taking off Brahma's fifth head to protect Brahmi, which resulted in the former being cursed to beg with Brahma's skull until Annapoorani filled it up.

Asurendran

*A*surendran, meanwhile, stormed into the court of Surapadma. In front of him was Surapadma, sitting majestically on his throne, discussing some minor affair with his minister. Ajamukhi occupied another throne, looking bored after having cried for days over the death of her sons, which her brother assured her would be looked into. Her eyes were red and swollen.

Asurendran did not waste a second and ran to the feet of Surapadma, hugging it tight, all the while crying his heart out. Surapadma did not even notice Asurendran's entrance and was confused at some Asura hugging his feet. Sura was the kindest among emperors when it came to matters concerning Asuras. He lifted him up and was shocked to see his wounded, bruised, teary-eyed nephew.

He said, 'What happened my son? Who did this to you? Was it Agastya who did this to my other nephews? I will send out Banugopan immediately and finish Agastya's story!'

'No, Uncle! Father is dead. Mayapuri has been burnt to the ground. The empire under my father has been taken over and is now ruled by Jwala!' ranted Asurendran.

'Have you gone mad? Amoghan! Get the physician to attend to Asurendran immediately. He seems to have lost his senses,' said Sura in an amused tone.

'I saved myself and ran here to warn you, my uncle, and I am being called mad. I should have died with my father!' said Asurendran in anger.

'There must be some truth in what Asurendran says,' said Ajamukhi. 'You did not take it seriously when my children were killed by Agastya. You did not take it seriously when Tarakasura sent me off here, sensing danger. Now, when your nephew comes here and says everything is done, you mock him!'

Seeing that both his sister and nephew were far from joking and the matter was something more serious, Sura said, 'Asure! Calm down. First sit, relax, have a drink of water or Soma and tell me what happened in detail.'

Amoghan wisely not only arranged for Soma, but also got Vajrabahu, who was Asurendran's friend and the physicians, for he knew that what Asurendran was about to say might be more important than what Sura was anticipating.

Asurendran pushed aside the Soma that was offered to him. He sat down on the floor with Vajrabahu next to him and started to narrate, 'Everything was normal when the day began with the sunrise. Then, bad omens overshadowed Mayapuri. We simply brushed them aside. Suddenly, without warning, Mayapuri was stormed by Gana forces, led by someone named Veera or something. They did not hesitate for a moment and went on a rampage. Our Asura armies attacked them and fought well.

'Unfortunately, our general, Mahadheera had been tasked by our father to take the best unit and go to finish the Agastya menace. Our existing force, without our general, was no match for the invaders. Father himself intervened, as did I. We fought valiantly. However, they kept on coming from the inside. They also freed the Devas who fought with them. Jwala too came in and started to burn down the city to the ground. Father fought long and hard. At one point, he reverted to his true monstrous form and jumped at the Ganas.

'However, again from the inside, one more person named Veera something jumped out. He fought Father so well that Father had to take out his best Astras. I decided to leave the battlefield to get reinforcements and our general back. When we came back, Father and Krauncha had sandwiched the Gana forces between them. We took Father's side, sure of victory with Mahadheera and Krauncha on either side supporting Father. Then, a spear came in and killed both Krauncha and Mahadheera in one stroke. Father then fought hard with the boy who threw the spear. He even used Pasupatastra and Sudarshan Chakra. None of them worked on the boy. The boy then killed father with the very same spear. I ran out of the field and tried to go to Mayapuri. It was razed to the ground while the women and children were kept safe. Not a single adult Asura warrior was left alive. Jwala was sitting on Father's throne, giving orders to the Devas and Agni's army.

'I left the place quickly and came running to you to tell you everything and warn you.'

'Are you high? Are you are telling me that a boy with a spear not only killed Krauncha and Mahadheera but also your father, who was in his true monstrous form, after he had been defeated by someone whose name is unknown to us? Is this a joke? Did your father set you up to it?' asked Sura as he turned to Amoghan.

'No, your majesty. I just confirmed with our spies. The young prince is not lying. His highness Tarakasura, the infallible demon Krauncha, the peerless general Mahadheera and their city Mayapuri are all no more. The only Asura men of your clan left there are the three five-year-old children of Tarakasura, who are now living with the high queen, Surasai, learning the arts from her,' said Amoghan. 'I also just received another bad news. There has been some activity in Chendur Kadu on the seashore, that is not of Asuric nature.'

Amoghan was not known for his sense of humour. He was known for his efficiency and wisdom. Sura took his words seriously and said, 'Vajrabahu, take Asurendran to your quarters. Also, have the physicians attend to him and his needs.' He then turned to Ajamukhi and said, 'Leave with them. I will call you if we need your help.' He turned to his guard and said, 'Summon Banugopan and our general here, now.'

Once they all left and Banugopan arrived with the general, Sura turned to Amoghan and asked him to elaborate. Amoghan repeated what had happened there, as gathered from Asurendran, in addition to the information gathered from the spies. He then went on to give his opinion of the current situation.

'Mayapuri has fallen. The emperor, the general and the protector of Mayapuri have fallen as well. The Asura empire has fallen by one-third officially, with us losing the power centre. The emperor was given a proper burial as befits him. They were not only surprised but also strategically outdone by the enemy. Women and children were spared. Also, I received information that Agastya is now with a minor Gana division led by someone named Veeramartanda, gathering people rebelling against us.

'Outside our empire, there has been movement of our enemies in the barren Chendur Kadu, which is usually desolate and maintained so by our Rakshasas with their erratic raids. Taking it that the valiant emperor would order so, I have sent out our spies to investigate what the activity is. Based on our spies' input, the boy who killed your brother is named Muruga, one of the sons of Shiva. He is the one who beat the immortal Indra and powerful Vayu like they were nothing; he also broke Mount Meru into two as well as emptied the Milky Ocean. He is accompanied by nine warrior brothers who are also said to be sons of Shiva. The task assigned to the ten of them is to destroy you, your highness, and set the Devas free. Agni has switched his allegiance from your late brother to the sons of Shiva as well.

'Right now, what was Mayapuri is being ruled by Jwala who, through it, is now the regent of one-third of the multiverse that the Asura empire controlled directly or indirectly. Strangely, Asurapuri has been overseen in favour of our kingdom by the Gana army, if my guess, that the activity in Chendur Kadu is a siege attempt by them, is right.'

'You are not known to be wrong, Amoghan,' said Sura. He turned to his chief guard and said, 'Send out a message to Asurapuri and ask my brother Simhamukha to come over here. He too should know of the events that have transpired.'

Sura then went to his private quarters and tears rolled down his cheeks for his brother, Tarakasura.

Veerabahu

*M*eanwhile, Muruga ordered Veerabahu to be the messenger. He had been assigned the task of offering peace to Sura, not as a subordinate but as a superior power that has taken over and burned Mayapuri down and is currently laying siege to Veeramahendrapuri. He had to exercise maximum control upon himself, as instructed by Muruga, to not lose sight of the mission or jeopardize it by letting his innate bravado get the better of him. Muruga had also told him to meet the Devas in prison and let them know that their troubles would be over soon. Veerabahu offered that he would free the Devas and get them here with him but Muruga rejected the idea; he believed that those who had endured maximum punishment, should not come out as fugitives but as truly free people.

Veerabahu took off from Chendur Kadu and, on reaching the shore, thought of Muruga. He immediately took on a gigantic form and then took a giant leap off the shore. He foot landed on the seventh circle, Kandhaman. His step was more a bounce the than a landing: he was so powerful and full of vigour that his step, forcefully placed, simply submerged the island with its inhabitants, a few Rakshasas and the runaways from the conquest of the Gana army.

Veerabahu realized that he should not have landed in his giant form and reduced his size before landing in the sixth circle, known as Ilanka, meaning island. It was ruled by Veerasinghan.

'Who are you? How dare you enter the kingdom of Sura? You do not look like an Asura. Only Asuras, the valiant ones, are allowed in here!' said Veerasinghan.

Though angered at the perceived insult, Veerabahu was not one to forget the orders of his lord. He said, 'I am Veerabahu, the messenger of Muruga, the general of the Devas and the son of Mahadeva. I am on my way to meet Surapadma and share the message of my lord.'

Veerasinghan became angry and said, 'Deliver the message here and leave if you want to live. No one but an Asura shall enter Veeramahendrapuri.'

Veerabahu ignored him and started to take off. Veerasinghan was not one to let it go and started shooting a plethora of arrows at him. His soldiers too were ordered to do the same. They merely pestered Veerabahu. He adjudged the situation and took the call to finish them off, lest he should fail in the assigned task of carrying his lord's message to Surapadma. He took a gigantic form and with his bare hands brutally cleared out all the Asura soldiers, as well as Veerasinghan. Having decimated the armed forces on the island, he leapt up high in the sky and landed forcefully on Ilanka, leaving it with the same fate as that of Kandhaman island.

Without further ado, Veerabahu meted out the same treatment to the other three islands and their guardians, leaving no survivors or the islands. However, he slowed down when he reached the second circle. Unlike the others, this also housed common folk, women and children. He could hear babies crying. He decided that he could not do the same here, as he had done in other places. He downsized himself and landed quietly in this circle.

This circle was ruled by Ativeeran, the son of Yazhimugan. Ativeeran was someone who lived up to his name. He was a courageous and brave warrior. His soldiers attacked Veerabahu without even giving him a chance to tell them why he was there. To defend himself, Veerabahu gleefully did a job on them, killing them with his bare hands. He was however then faced by Ativeeran in a one on one battle.

On seeing that Veerabahu had no weapons, Ativeeran dropped

his too, and pounced on Veerabahu. They fought bare handed for some time. Veerabahu came to respect Ativeeran's prowess as well as sense of fairness. After engaging him, Veerabahu decided that he had had enough and had wasted enough time, so he ripped Ativeeran's hands off, hoping that he would back off. Ativeeran would rather die than retreat, so without a choice and with a heavy heart, Veerabahu finally snapped Ativeeran's neck, finishing him off.

Veerabahu then took off to the next circle, ruled by the dreaded Yazhimugan. He had the face of a Yazhi, which looked like a cross between a dragon and an elephant, and was one of the original Asuras who had come into being along with Sura. He commanded immense respect from Sura, so much so that he was given the command of the first circle.

Setting his eyes on Veerabahu and seeing all the blood on him, Yazhimugan realized that he definitely would have killed off his son. Angrily, he charged at him, but Veerabahu dodged him completely as he uprooted a tree. Veerabahu and Yazhimugan sparred with a tree and a mace for a weapon. Unlike the previous challenges, Yazhimugan was incredibly strong. They fought long and hard, with each gaining the upper hand alternately. At one point, Veerabahu realized that he was wasting time and becoming diverted from the mission. He called up Muruga in his mind, gathered all his power and in one powerful stroke hit Yazhimugan on his chest. Yazhimugan fell to the ground. Veerabahu then jumped up into the sky and landed squarely on his, chest finishing him off.

Yazhimugan's battle took a lot out of Veerabahu, but he was finally able to enter Veeramahendrapuri.

Veerabahu was spellbound by its lavish beauty and ornate architecture. He had never seen anything so beautiful. Mayapuri was the first city that he had admired, for Kailash is more known for its serenity and natural beauty than its richness. If one were to say that Mayapuri was beautiful, Veeramahendrapuri was a hundred-thousand-fold more so. It was as if Surapadma was not only a better and stronger warrior than Tarakasura, but he was also someone with excellent taste and was well-versed in the knowledge of the arts. Veerabahu immediately felt sad. All of this would be destroyed and would sink into the ocean in a few days.

The security was elaborate and Veerabahu could not find a way to enter incognito into the city, let alone the palace. Unfortunately, or fortunately for Veerabahu, he came across Gajamugan at the south entrance. He had been tasked to review and beef up the security, based on the recent developments, by Sura himself. He spotted Veerabahu.

'Stop! You are not an Asura. You do not belong here. Seeing your bloodied appearance, it is quite clear that you have killed Ativeeran and Yazhimugan and did not come here incognito. You have come to your death!' said Gajamugan, charging towards him along with the guards. Veerabahu sidestepped Gajamugan and did a quick and a quiet job on the guards. Before he could turn around, he was shoved off forcefully by Gajamugan, who came charging at him from behind.

Veerabahu moved forward quite a few steps before he stopped himself. He turned around but was caught by a humongous boulder thrown by Gajamugan. Veerabahu quickly punched the boulder splitting it into a thousand pieces. He, on his part, uprooted a giant peepal tree, which pushed Gajamugan a few steps backwards. Then they ran at each other full force, throwing punches. Veerabahu cleverly dodged a punch from Gajamugan while landing his punch flatly on his opponent's forehead. He then kicked him hard in the heart and repeated what he had done to Yazhimugan, thereby finishing Gajamugan off.

Veerabahu then diminished his size to that of a bee, taking its form and flying into the city through the south gate. He traversed the city and finally reached the palace, using the giant flag mast at the centre of the city for direction. He reached the palace gates and saw that it was guarded by two gigantic Asuras whose heavily scarred bodies showed how battle toughened they were. These Asuras were Vairan and Mayuran. Not wanting to raise an alarm, he quietly buzzed past them and hid in the garden for dawn to come.

Until dawn, Veerabahu flew around the palace, noting down its structure, as he had done with the city. Once dawn broke, he buzzed around the courtroom, waiting to hear the announcement that Surapadma was there.

Negotiations

$\mathcal{V}$eerabahu buzzed inside the palace. It was built magnificently, with only six ways in. One entrance was directly from Sura's family quarters, meant for the first family, and for the rest of them, there was another. The way in through for the rest of the folk was through a museum with gigantic statues of warriors who had fallen in wars fought for Asura supremacy and paintings which depicted the legacy of the emperor he is about to meet. If one were to come through the museum entrance, by the time they reached the courtroom of the Asura king, they would be awestruck by his legacy and legend.

The courtroom by itself was simple. It was circular in shape and five elevated thrones were placed along half the room, with a gigantic statue of Mahadeva behind the throne at the centre— Sura's throne. The sixth one was at the edge of this half of the room, with a slightly lower elevation. At the other edge were two smaller seats for the general and minister, placed at ground level. Veerabahu realized that Sura had not forgotten that everything he had was by the will of the supreme lord. The rest of them, no matter who they are, are to stand and do the business they came in for, unless Sura offered them a seat on the higher plane. Loud thumps echoed in the room, getting louder by the minute. It was constructed in such a manner that it ensured that the visitor, if it was the enemy, merely by the sound of the footsteps, knew that they had taken on a challenge they could only hope to survive.

Sura came in, worshipped the gargantuan idol behind him and sat on the throne. He was followed by Simhamukha and Banugopan, who came in from their respective quarters. Once they were seated, Simhamukha and Sura looked at each other and Simhamukha nodded at him. Sura then said, 'Who are you?'

This confused the general, minister and the guards. Their emperor knew who they were.

'We know you are here. Tell us who you are before we squash you like the bee in which form you are!' thundered Simhamukha.

Veerabahu was taken aback. He was hiding inside a flowerpot as a bee. Not one other person in the room had even noticed him as a bee, let alone realize that he was more than a bee. Banugopan immediately armed himself, as did the general Bhaagasura.

'If you are here by mistake, tell me your identity, the purpose of your visit and you might just leave the courtroom alive, for I have a lot to do and do not want to waste time. Waste a moment more and you will be squashed and finished off,' said Sura. His voice was not only majestic, deep and powerful, but also had an element of kindness, for Sura realized that someone who could do this Maya so efficiently might be an Asura himself and possibly a student of his mother or his guru.

Veerabahu buzzed to the centre of the courtroom. He prayed to his lord and revealed himself.

'My name is Veerabahu,' he said, introducing himself. 'I am the general of lord Muruga, the general of the Devas, son of Mahadeva and Mahashakti and the god of victory. I am here to complete the task assigned by him as his messenger.'

'Your god of victory did well to send his general as his messenger, realizing that he alone had the best chance of getting out alive. I, however, bow to only one god and he is always behind me. Now that you are here, do your assigned task, give your message and leave before I change my mind,' said Sura.

'I am not sure if Sura and his clan know how to treat a messenger. One should receive the messenger, give him a seat, refreshments and then ask him for the message,' said Veerabahu.

'No one but an Asura will ever sit inside this courtroom. Besides, you did not come in as a messenger, but unannounced as a bee. The message, or leave,' said Sura.

'I, the general of Muruga, will not deliver a message standing,' said Veerabahu. He closed his eyes, said Muruga's name and instantly, a throne of the same design, dimension and magnitude of Sura's appeared behind him at the centre of the courtroom. He sat on the high throne, at the same height as Sura. Banugopan was incensed and he prepared to lunge towards him but was stopped by Sura.

'My mother is Maya. I have seen better tricks. This is the last time I am asking you. The message or death!' said Sura.

'Here is the message, for I do not want to kill any more of you, lest I fail in my mission of delivering the message to Sura, on account of his death at the hands of a mere messenger.

'Lord Muruga, the god of victory, in his capacity as the general of the Devas and leader of Ganas, hereby commands you to surrender unconditionally and seek refuge at his feet. He also officially informs you that, as we speak, you are under siege. He also orders you to release all the Devas from captivity and treat them fairly as equals and compatriots. Failing to comply with the above two would not only mean certain death for Sura and his clan but to the entire race of Asuras who stemmed from Maya. However, if complied with, Lord Muruga assures on the name of his father, Mahadeva, that the lives of Sura and his clan and his kingdom will survive and will continue as it has done thus far.

'As proof and evidence for the might of Lord Muruga and his army, the place known as Mayapuri, along with its warrior subjects and its emperor, were slaughtered within half a day by his prowess and strategy. As proof and evidence for his kindness, the women and children were not only spared but were protected and are treated better than they were under the erstwhile emperor,' finished Veerabahu.

Banugopan and Bhaagasura were irate upon hearing this. All except Sura wielded their weapons once Veerabahu mentioned the name of Mayapuri.

'You can leave. Tell your lord that if he were to surrender to me unconditionally, I will spare his life and will allow him the honour of being my footstool for eternity. Even that privilege is given for he is the son of my lord. You can be my son's footstool, for no one in the last millennia had the courage to be inside Sura's courtroom, let alone talk the way you did,' said Sura. Simhamukha laughed insultingly, intentionally.

It was Veerabahu's turn to lose his temper. Sura's ploy had worked. He could not touch a messenger, but he could touch an assailant.

'You vile Sura! How dare you speak of my lord that way!' said Veerabahu as he created a scythe out of thin air. 'You will now face the same fate as Gajamugan, Ativeeran, Yazhimugan, Veerasinghan and the rest of your Asura warriors.'

As soon as Veerabahu stepped down from the throne, Muruga, who knew all that is there to know, appeared in his mind and asked him to restrain himself and behave as befits a messenger. Veerabahu calmed down, the scythe disappeared, and he said, 'According to the order of my lord, I will spare all your lives. This is war: in seven days, there will be no Asura clan left.' He then disappeared from the palace, reappearing outside. His rage at the insult to his lord had not gone away, and he took it all out on the buildings and quarters surrounding the palace, making sure that no one was hurt.

On Veerabahu mentioning the deaths of so many valiant and respected warriors, Sura lost his temper. Banugopan said that he would go out and finish him, but Sura stopped him, saying that someone of Banugopan's stature should not be required for this task. He summoned Vajrabahu and told him to bring Veerabahu alive, so that he can be taught some manners before being finished off.

Vajrabahu took his army division and sent them in different directions in the city to search for Veerabahu, while he went to the palace garden. Sura, of course, had warned him that Veerabahu is capable of wielding Maya and asked him to be alert.

Vajrabahu

*V*eerabahu was busy taking out his wrath on the palace garden of Sura. As his attention turned to the flag pillar, an arrow shot past him, hit him and fell down lifeless. He turned around and saw Vajrabahu, the son of Surapadma. Vajrabahu and Banugopan were among the few of Surapadma's sons who took their legacy seriously and sought to extend the reign of the Asura empire beyond Surapadma's time.

Seeing Vajrabahu, Veerabahu said, 'Leave! I have no intention of ending another Asura. I will spare your life. One more arrow in my direction would mean certain death for you. Nowhere does it say that a messenger cannot defend himself. I will rip you apart and take out my wrath on you, and you will incur the same fate as the rest of your guardian warriors.'

'Come with me with your hands bound and I shall leave. I have orders to take you alive. Else, you would be dead already,' said Vajrabahu.

'I will give you one more chance. Take your best shot at me. After that, I shall not hold back and I promise you that your death will be the most painful or I am not the son of Mahashakti!' said Veerabahu.

Vajrabahu took out a special Astra, given to him by his

grandmother. He aimed it at Veerabahu's heart, and it hit its target perfectly.

Veerabahu laughed his heart out and said, 'My lord, Muruga, resides in my heart. Not even the most powerful of Astras can touch me as long as he is there. You have shot your last arrow!'

Saying this, he pounced on Vajrabahu like a famished tiger pounces on its prey, but Vajrabahu sidestepped, hitting Veerabahu in the back and making him even angrier. They clasped each other's hand and tried to push each other back using their full might. Veerabahu was little surprised, for he found Vajrabahu to be much stronger and much more agile than the Asuras he had killed so far on his way to Surapadma. It was a show of might between the two and as the two planted their feet firmly on the ground, their feet started to dig in deep, sourcing all the power they could muster at each other.

Veerabahu cleverly took a step back, spread his hands outwards and hit Vajrabahu's chest hard with his chest, throwing him off balance. Vajrabahu fell to the ground, as did his crown. This enraged him: he had never been beaten one on one and nothing but his feet had touched the ground thus far. He lunged at Veerabahu, who went under him, lifted him with both hands and threw him hard at the fountainhead in the centre of Surapadma's garden, breaking it into a thousand pieces.

Veerabahu pounced on him again but Vajrabahu caught his hands, and with his legs on his chest, threw him across the garden. Veerabahu landed hard on the ground, shattering the beautiful tile pattern. He was shocked at the might of Vajrabahu. As Veerabahu got up, Vajrabahu landed in front of him and took him up in a bear hug, crushing his ribs. Veerabahu struggled initially but then he clapped his hands over the ears of Vajrabahu multiple times, sending his ears ringing. As he got free from Vajrabahu, he jumped and landed a few steps back, before falling down.

When he got up and turned, he was caught by a huge tree that fell on his chest, throwing him to the ground again while Vajrabahu jumped on him pushing the tree down Veerabahu's chest. They both used all their might to gain the upper hand, but the tree was mostly stationary for they were evenly matched. This stalemate was taking a lot out of both the warriors. Veerabahu realized that he was wasting valuable time and getting diverted from his original mission. The war had not started yet.

Taking a deep breath, Veerabahu thought of his lord, Muruga, shouted 'Vetri Vel, Veera Vel!', and headbutted the tree, breaking it into smithereens and then throwing Vajrabahu hard on the ground. Vajrabahu had splinters from the tree lodged all over his face and body as he fell down. The dust from the broken tree blinded him as well.

Veerabahu then jumped up to the sky, grew in stature to the size he used when he killed Gajamugan and landed with all his might, hard over Vajrabahu's heart. It was smashed and became one with the earth he was on. His chest now had the imprint of Veerabahu's feet. Vajrabahu's legs kicked a few times before they stopped completely, along with his heart.

Vajrabahu was dead and all of Veerabahu's aggression had been taken out. He stood silently for a moment. He looked around, took a flower and placed it over his chest. He had the satisfaction of fighting a worthy opponent who went toe to toe with him. After paying his respects to a warrior unparalleled, Veerabahu took off in the form of a butterfly towards the second circle, where the prison of the Devas was located.

Meanwhile, Vajrabahu's regiment, which had gone in search of Veerabahu, returned and were shocked to see their valiant and unparalleled leader on the ground, dead. They let out a wail as one of them ran to inform Surapadma of his beloved son's fate.

Jayanta

*T*he Devas in the prison were with Jayanta at that moment. They generally assembled there during this time, which was a break for the Asura guards, who were usually busy torturing them. They hoped and tried their best to revive their general and prince, but all of their efforts were in vain.

A butterfly floated inside and landed on Jayanta. The Devas waited for some time to see if Jayanta would react. He did not move a muscle and they shooed it off.

The butterfly flew to the middle of the cell and transformed into Veerabahu. The Devas immediately shielded Jayanta, covering him from all sides, fearing that this was a new Asura who had come to punish them even more.

'Do not fear,' said Veerabahu. 'I am Veerabahu, son of Mahadeva, general of Muruga, who has been appointed general of the Deva and Gana armies, for the sole purpose of putting an end to the Asura race and freeing the Devas. The time has come for you all to be set free.'

Jayanta's eyes usually registered everything and sent the information to his brain, which simply had given up and chose to ignore all the inputs. It was the same with all other sensory organs of his. But, upon seeing a stranger come in and do the same trick that he had once fallen for, his brain could not hold back any longer and it burst into activity.

'No!' shouted Jayanta. 'No! No! This is a trick. It is the same trick being played on us again. We are being taken for a ride again. This is Surapadma himself, who has come to play with our psyche again. The mind games have gone far enough, Sura! We know you. We know that my father, Indra, is a coward who has long forsaken us. We know that our suffering makes no difference to Mahadeva or Mahavishnu. We know that our fate is sealed, and our future is doomed for eternity.

'We know that you will forever rule the multiverse unchallenged and there is no stopping you. Why do you have to toy with us? Is it not enough, all the torture you have made the Devas endure? Is it not enough that our Deva women are now mere concubines for the lowest of creatures? Is it not enough for you that we have accepted defeat? Why do you have to play with our fragile minds over and over again? What is there to break? We are already broken! You cannot fool us over and over again. Leave now! I beg of you. Leave us alone. Let your minions have their fun with us. Let them tear us apart limb from limb! Leave us to our misery and misfortune. No more, Sura! No more!'

The Devas were saddened at the state of their leader. They didn't buy it either. Veerabahu pitied them for how far they had been pushed.

'The amount of pain and torture you had to endure at the hands of the Asuras has pushed you to such desperation. Heed my words: Muruga, born of Shiva's third eye, came into being for the sole purpose of finishing off the Asura clan that came from Surasai. We came with him to aid him in this purpose. Indra, your father, has commissioned Muruga as the general for the task officially. We have already killed Tarakasura and destroyed Mayapuri, freeing the Devas in captivity there. They too have joined us in the mission. We also have freed all the kingdoms enroute from the tyranny of the Asuras, who are joining our quest to end the Asura race.

'I have also killed Vajrabahu, son of Surapadma, on my way here, as well as Gajamugan, the chief of staff of the Asura. Ativeeran, Yazhimugan, Veerasinghan are also dead. There is no circle of defence left for Surapadma.

'I am here on a mission as Muruga's messenger to give Surapadma a chance to reform and set you free. As one would expect, he refused the offer. The war will commence tomorrow. I swore an oath on Muruga's name that in six days, there would not be a single Asura warrior left who came of Surasai.

'I can set you free and take you with me now, except that after being the martyr and victim of so much pain and torture, Muruga felt that your freedom should be brought only after complete victory over the Asura clan. You need not trust me now. You can count the days and the seventh day from tomorrow, you will be free citizens of the multiverse with no fear,' said Veerabahu kindly.

'We do not know whether to believe you or not. We, however, believe in our leader, Jayanta,' said the Devas as they turned to him. 'Like you said, we will know in seven days. Even though you claim that this island is free from Ativeeran, we will not come out.'

'I have a request,' said Jayanta.

'Ask!' said Veerabahu.

'Can we see this Muruga?' asked Jayanta.

Veerabahu took a step back, grew in stature and took the form of Muruga, thinking of him deep in his heart, complete with six heads, eighteen eyes and twelve hands wielding different weapons, including the Sudarshan Chakra and the Vel. They were awestruck by the beauty, grace and bowed before the figure. Veerabahu disappeared, turning into a butterfly.

Samudra

*A*s the drama was unfolding in the Asura empire, Muruga and the other brothers were not sitting on their hands. Vishwakarma, Brahma, Narada, the Navagrahas and whoever was held against their wishes, or only because Sura was not capable of killing them and were too important to be imprisoned, left Veeramahendrapuri and came to Chendur Kadu after the Veerabahu incident in the courtroom. Veerakesari too had returned with a massive army, collecting every single Deva who had been festering thoughts of vengeance for centuries.

Muruga ordered Vishwakarma and the brothers to build a massive fort and reinforcements after creating a massive island where the third circle had originally stood. They were, however, challenged by Samudra, the ocean king who was a willing slave of Surapadma. In spite of numerous attempts by Vishwakarma to build such an island, Samudra repeatedly kept sinking their structure using tsunami waves. Upon hearing it, Veerakesari was irate. He took his bow and arrow, vowing to kill Samudra.

Samudra, the king of oceans, carried a trident akin to Mahadeva, in utter devotion to him. Indra, while living in Amaravati, had no need for Samudra, and with Indra, if he has no need for you, you get nothing from him. Samudra did not even get appointments to meet with the erstwhile ruler of the universe, unlike he did with Daksha who was his brother. Samudra was left to face his troubles all by himself. Sura, on the other hand, treated him with respect, for their relationship was symbiotic and mutually beneficial. Sura needed Samudra to both build as well as protect Veeramahendrapuri. Samudra needed Sura to protect him and back him when he was trying to protect his resources and subjects.

'How dare this Samudra keep stopping us, us who killed and erased Mayapuri from the map of the multiverse in a matter of minutes! I will not only destroy him but also his kingdom and subjects. I swear on your name!' said Veerakesari to Muruga.

Muruga said with his ever-present smile, 'Killing someone is easy, Veerakesari, especially for someone as powerful as you. Sparing one, even though we have the power to end the person, takes real grace, power and skill. Samudra is merely doing his duty to his ruler as he did to his then ruler, Indra. His real intention is to ensure the well-being of his subjects. If we were to intimidate them enough, he would automatically help us with our task. Life is precious. We should not take one so long as we have a choice. When Mahadeva gave us power, remember that the power he gave us is for protecting as many lives as possible, not taking them at our whim and fancy. There would be no difference between Sura and us if we were to do the same.'

Muruga then ventured to the seashore and summoned Samudra, who appeared and said, 'Forgive me, son of Shiva. I am bound by duty to my emperor, Sura, to protect his kingdom. I cannot allow a construction which is built with the intention to threaten the very kingdom I have sworn to protect. You will have to kill me if you want to proceed with the construction.'

Muruga smiled and said, 'There is no intention or need to kill you, someone who is merely bound by duty, to stop you from performing it. You have my utmost respect for your sense of duty and gratitude. I seek your forgiveness for what I am about to do to you.'

Muruga then took his Vel, whispered something to its head and threw it into the ocean. The ocean immediately dried up, leaving just enough water for sea life to survive, while leaving enough room for Vishwakarma and the Veera brothers to resume their work. Samudra was taken aback by the massive display of power by a small boy. He tried his best to raise a wave but realized that he could not do so without killing off his subjects, the sea life to which he had a higher duty.

He realized that the person in front of him was no ordinary boy and was more than merely a son of Shiva. He was a powerful being in his own right, equal to Shiva. Samudra would not have been impressed if Muruga had dried out the ocean completely. He was impressed by the fact that Muruga was able to exercise enough control to dry out just the right amount of water to balance the need of the sea life as well as his want of building a fortress to house his soldiers and conduct war.

He turned to Muruga and said, 'I concede defeat to you. I also thank you for not drying out the ocean completely, even though you are fully capable of it, and sparing the life of my subjects.'

Veerakesari said, 'His peacock once drank up the entire Milky Ocean at his command. Your ocean is nothing for him. But for his grace, your kingdom would have met the same fate as destined for Veeramahendrapuri and Asurapuri.'

Samudra bowed to Muruga, who blessed him. He then asked Vishwakarma to resume his work, taking the aid of Brahma and the Veera brothers.

Samudra meanwhile took leave and ran to Sura's courtroom to apprise him of the development, as he was duty bound to do so. Muruga let him go, for this might be the factor that would make Sura realize that Muruga is not a mere boy but death itself for the Asura clan. He wanted to give as many chances as possible, for Sura was a devotee of Mahadeva.

Mourning

*W*hen Samudra entered Veeramahendrapuri, he was shocked. This was not the city he had visited often and had come to admire. The city was broken. People were in mourning, trying to make sense of the wanton destruction let loose on them by Veerabahu both before and during his duel with their beloved prince Vajrabahu, which ultimately cost the latter's life. Vajrabahu was the only one who could stand up to Banugopan in might and was on call to become what Simhamukha was to Surapadma, an able equal brother who stood by him no matter what. The very idea that he could be killed was something the people could not digest.

Samudra went on towards the palace and as he neared it, the destruction got worse. The last time he had seen destruction on such a scale had been during Daksha's yagna, after it was ransacked by Veerabhadra and Bhadrakali.

At the heart of the city, there was a huge funeral pyre, with

Surapadma holding the flaming torch as he prepared to cremate his son Vajrabahu and his friend Gajamugan along with Veerasinghan, Yazhimugan and Ativeeran. The women and men of the Asura folk were standing and mourning. The women were wailing, singing songs of praise, courage and bravery of the legendary warriors. Being a kind king when it came to the Asuras, he took it upon himself to do the last rites not only for his son but also for those who were slain by Veerabahu. This was the first time he ever had to hold the flaming torch in his existence that spanned millennia.

Upon seeing Samudra, Surapadma, still teary, summoned him and went into the courtroom along with Banugopan, Simhamukha, Amoghan, Asurendran and Agnimukha. His first task was to appoint Banugopan his general in place of the slain Gajamugan.

Amoghan was the first to speak: 'Grieve, my emperor, for if you do, it will clear you of all thought of vengeance. Vengeance is a very evil emotion when it comes to war, which is why it is prohibited. No one should enter into war seeking vengeance, for it will run amok over common sense and will render the wearer powerless and without self-control.'

'Enough!' shouted Banugopan. 'I will seek vengeance. I will pursue this Veerabahu and tear him apart limb by limb while killing him slowly. I will ensure that he will experience every ounce of pain that my beloved brother had to go through.'

'I will come with you and I will ensure that not a single one of the races that did this to our brother survive. They will pay and will go through the same excruciating pain that our brother experienced. I will kill them all with my bare hands,' said Agnimukha. Asurendran was equally incensed.

'This is precisely why we should listen to Amoghan even more,' said a voice, shocking Surapadma. He wanted to turn and see who the coward was and was appalled at the sight of Simhamukha. The fearless Simhamukha, who presided over the multiverse, was speaking like he was afraid.

Simhamukha understood the meaning of Surapadma's expression and went on to elaborate: 'Do not mistake my caution for fear, Brother. You must first understand the magnitude of the enemy's power before going on to make claims of superiority. When we took over the multiverse, we were underestimated and our enemies were underprepared for us. We should not commit the same mistake, being the rulers of the multiverse.

'The enemy is more than a mere boy. He is the son of our lord, Mahadeva, who gave us the boons. He would not have come here to fight us without Mahadeva's consent and blessings. Has Mahadeva decided that our time is up? The boon we got, remember, is that we can only be killed by Mahadeva's power. What better way to cast out one's ultimate power than through his offspring?

'The people killed by Veerabahu, who we did not know of until he came here, were no ordinary Asuras. Gajamugan and Yazhimugan had fought by our side since the first great war. Veerasinghan and Ativeeran were no less warriors whose bravery was so well respected by you that you gave them their own kingdoms. Above all, Vajrabahu was so unparalleled in speed and power that Vayu would not be able to overtake him. If all these exceptional epitomes of prowess were defeated by someone who claims to be a mere messenger of Muruga, a small boy, you should estimate the power the small boy possesses and prepare accordingly. Not to forget that this boy killed not only Mahadheera and Krauncha but also our brother Tarakasura, who fought Mahavishnu to a stalemate, within hours.

'We have no axe to grind against Mahadeva. You are still as devoted to him as I am. If we were to approach him and repledge our allegiance to him, he would still grant us with many more boons and take Muruga and his army off our backs. After all, everything we got, everything we are, all of it came from him.'

'Shut up!' growled Surapadma. He went on to chastise Simhamukha, saying, 'Are you asking me to surrender to an enemy who is merely a boy and is backed by the very Devas we defeated?

Are you asking me to do so after he has killed my son and brother? You were always a softie and worshipping Kali has made you softer! I would not be shocked if you were killed off by an ordinary Gana in Muruga's army with a single shot! I am ashamed of you!'

'But there is a point in what your brother is...' started Amoghan but was quietened by the angry stare of Sura.

'As your brother, it is my duty to look after your best interests. Listen to me very carefully. I am willing to fight for you and die, even if I am weaker than an ordinary soldier in Muruga's army, without the slightest of hesitation.

'There is no victory for you in this war. If you win, you will get a bad name for having fought against and killed a small boy. Further, killing the son of the supreme lord is a sure-fire way to incur his wrath and I honestly believe that you do not think that you are capable of fighting, let alone defeating, Mahadeva. If you lose or worse, die, your name will carry the stain of having lost to a small boy. The valiant Surapadma, the ruler of the multiverse, the emperor of the worlds, losing to a small boy. Imagine that!

'I have had my say. Your decision is my decision. As Kali wills, I will fight the war with you and die for you. The next course of action is entirely up to you,' concluded Simhamukha.

Surapadma realized that Simhamukha did have a point. He said, 'Amoghan, get Vishwakarma and Brahma to repair the city. Banugopan, prepare to attack the enemy tomorrow at dawn. If anyone has anything to say, this will be final opportunity.'

Amoghan opened his mouth. Sura turned to him, asking him to speak his mind. Amoghan said, 'Our spies have returned. All the Devas, rishis, Vasus, Navagrahas have surrendered to Muruga. They are also building a fortress in the middle of the ocean not far off from here to commence the war. Going by the preparation, their plan is to attack tomorrow.'

Surapadma immediately turned his attention to Samudra in shock. How could Samudra, someone he respected, allow an enemy to build a fortress? Samudra did not wait and spoke, 'Do not doubt my allegiance to you Sura. I stopped their attempt seven times and did not allow them to raise an inch of land. But this Muruga, son of Shiva, as told by his general, had his peacock drink up the Milky Ocean itself. He cast his Vel and the ocean dried up. He also left just enough water to spare my subjects as well. He is not only powerful, brave and wise but also kind. He spared my life and allowed me to come to you and inform you personally, lest you take me for a traitor.'

Surapadma was going through a gamut of confusing emotions. He turned to Amoghan and said, 'Get Vishwakarma and Brahma from a different universe and get them to rebuild the ruined city as well as construct a fortress around the city.' He then turned to Banugopan and said, 'You already have my orders, General.'. Banugopan was pleased and left with Agnimukha and Asurendran to prepare for war. Simhamukha took leave to go to Asurapuri to summon his forces to back his beloved brother.

Prathama

$\mathscr{T}$he lower eastern sky turned red. It was the dawn of the first day in Kritika month. This was the moment Muruga had chosen to bring an end to the dominion of the Asuras over the multiverse.

Muruga and his full army stood in their newly created fortress in the middle of the ocean. It was named Skandamadana. Its beauty rivalled Veeramahendrapuri. Samudra, as per the orders of Surapadma, had cleared the gigantic space in the middle of the ocean between Veeramahendrapuri and the new island, installed as per Muruga's orders, giving Surapadma and Muruga an open battlefield to fight the second great war, with the future of the multiverse on the line.

Veerabahu and his brothers, except for Veeramartanda who was away, were anxious to go all out, but were held back by Muruga.

Soon, a deafening noise engulfed the whole ocean. It came from Veeramahendrapuri. Hundreds of thousands of Kombu (a long war horn) and Murasu (wide war drum) started playing in unison, striking fear in all the living creatures in the surrounding area. The noise was heard as far as Kailash. It, however, did not deter Muruga or his army one bit.

Muruga waited out until the proclamation of war by the enemy was complete. Then he took out his Vamavrata, the Shankha of his father, the supreme lord. He put it to his mouth and blew it from the depth of his lungs. This sound drowned out any and every noise in all of the multiverse, evoking fear and sending shockwaves. The whole of Veeramahendrapuri, being closest to the source of the noise, drowned in fear, except for Surapadma. In Asurapuri, any doubts Simhamukha might have had about their end being near were cleared upon hearing the noise. Even Mahadeva, while engrossed in his meditation, heard the noise and smiled. Nandi and Ganesha were jubilant for the war had started and the world would soon realize the true might of their lord, Mahadeva, through his son. Whatever morale was boosted by the playing of the Kombu and Murasu by the Asuras was flattened by the sound of the Vamavrata.

Muruga finished blowing his Vamavrata and signalled Veerabahu to lead the forces into the battlefield. Banugopan, followed by Asurendran and Agnimukha, quickly recuperated from the effects of the Shankha, gathered their army and left for the battlefield as well. Surapadma was on his throne, with Amoghan standing by. He had also released Samudra from his service, in spite of Samudra's repeated pledges to die for Surapadma if needed, and left him as a neutral observant, for he did not want Samudra to suffer in any way as a consequence of the battle that will be fought between the two forces. The sound of the Shankha made it clear to Surapadma that Muruga had indeed come here with the blessings of Mahadeva.

Banugopan had arranged his army in an infantry circle with his brothers Asurendran and Agnimukha leading perpendicular to him. Veerabahu went in with a standard double echelon, aiming to pierce through the circular formation. His intention was to finish off the weaker army that has come and go straight for Veeramahendrapuri. His brothers led each point like arrows. Muruga had handed over the reins of strategizing this leg of the war to Veerabahu, but cryptically told him to replicate the opponent's strategy if need be. He also held back two divisions under Veerakesari and Veerandhaka. This confused Veerabahu because he saw no need for this, since he did not think the enemy was worthy of extensive strategy.

As soon as Veerabahu and Banugopan set eyes on each other, they gave marching orders by sounding their Shankha and ran at each other. Just as Banugopan and Veerabahu were about to meet head on, Banugopan pulled a fast one on his opponent and went past him with his division. Banugopan quickly took to the centre of the echelon while the other two brothers encircled the army of Ganas. Veerabahu had walked into a trap where he was now caught between two circles, Banugopan and his division on the inside and the other two brothers and their division on the outside.

Veerabahu's army were being attacked both from outside and inside. Quick to remember what Muruga had said, Veerabahu quickly gave the command and asked them to form a circle. From the aerial view, it was three concentric circles with Banugopan at the centre surrounded by the Ganas and Devas who were surrounded by Asurendran and Agnimukha's division, sandwiching Muruga's army.

While Veerabahu and his division were fighting Banugopan and his division, the other Veera brothers were fighting valiantly against the division led by Asurendran and Agnimukha, who had surrounded them. They were, at times, attacked by Banugopan's division as well. Muruga quickly sent out the two divisions that he had held back, who formed a circle covering the division led by Asurendran and Agnimukha. The tables were turned with

Agnimukha and Asurendran fighting two fronts while Banugopan and Veerabahu were fully engaged with each other. Asurendran and Agnimukha took on Veerandhaka and Veerakesari while the rest of the Veera brothers were ransacking the Asura army. They waged severe war for hours.

The fight between Banugopan and Veerabahu, however, was the centrepiece of the day. They were fighting their hearts out, raining arrows on each other, escalating the power with each shot. They were matched and, at different times, succeeded in disarming one another, only for the person to recover and carry on with even more vigour. After a point, the formations disappeared and Banugopan, backed by Agnimukha and Asurendran, went head on with Veerabahu, backed by Veerandhaka and Veerakesari.

Banugopan, now having realized that he had indeed underestimated his opponent, took his most powerful Astra, the Mohanastra, which had the capacity to incapacitate an entire army if aimed at the leader, rendering them immobile and practically making them sitting ducks.

With everyone including Veerabahu being immobile, the Asura forces started to have a field day with the Ganas and Devas. Banugopan, Asurendran and Agnimukha went after their targets, toying with them with swords and maces, reassured of their definite victory, aiming more to extract vengeance than to go for the kill.

Much to their chagrin, an Astra shot past them without touching them. It went over the Ganas and Devas and hit Banugopan. It was Muruga himself, in his magnificent chariot with Indra holding the reins. He had just shot an Amohanastra at his division, setting them free.

Banugopan turned around and saw the divine form of Muruga. He immediately wanted to fold his hands and worship him, for he believed he was seeing Mahadeva himself. With eighteen eyes and twelve hands, ten of them wielding weapons, including the Sudarshan Chakra, Trisula and Vel, and a face so beautiful, serene and pure, Muruga was the embodiment of divinity itself. The whole Asura army was spellbound by the magnificent and brilliant imagery that stood before them in the form of Muruga. It was as if they had been hit by a Mohanastra.

The Asura army had become complacent about their immobile enemy, and they all paid the price with their lives when their enemy's mobility returned, and the Ganas and Devas were wielding the best weapons that they had in their hands before they were rendered motionless.

Veerabahu, seeing the opportunity that his enemy Banugopan was not wielding any major weapon, wasted no time and took a Pasupatastra. Once Banugopan, Asurendran and Agnimukha saw the Pasupatastra, they realized that their doom was imminent. The three of them quickly disappeared from the battlefield using Maya. Seeing their general and leaders disappear from the battlefield, the Asura army became demoralized. They started running in all directions, aiming for Veeramahendrapuri. The Ganas and Devas finished off all of those they could get to before the Asura army was sent running with their proverbial tails between their legs.

The Ganas and Devas were jubilant and shouted 'Vetri Vel! Veera Vel!' shaking the battlefield as the sun set, ending the first day of the war.

Banugopan entered the city, his head hanging in shame. There was no one to welcome him. The city was deserted. The news had spread. He was undefeated. He was untouchable. He was the one pegged to take over the multiverse from his father. Yet, he had to run away from the battlefield like a coward to save his life.

Asurendran had faced this before. He quietly avoided meeting anyone and went to his quarters. Agnimukha was irate. He decided to do an elaborate sacrifice to invoke and please Goddess Bhadrakali and gain her favour for the next time he was going to enter the battlefield.

Banugopan was left alone to face the shame. He neared the

palace and his steps slowed further. He was engulfed in thought as to how to face his father, the most valiant Asura, and tell him that his son had run away from a battlefield, from an enemy he and his father considered so much inferior. His footsteps led him to the palace gates. He hesitated for a moment and then went through the rear entrance to his quarters. He could not sleep even for a moment. He walked into the courtroom. His father, the valiant Sura, was on the throne, getting updates from Amoghan.

Amoghan, upon seeing the prince, avoided eye contact and left the room quietly. Surapadma looked straight ahead while Banugopan's head was bent in shame. Both were waiting for the other to talk.

Banugopan simply said, 'If I do not defeat Veerabahu the next time I enter the battlefield, I will kill myself.' He then left his father's presence.

Surapadma was not impressed. He was irate. He was disappointed. He could not sleep. Words from Simhamukha and Amoghan kept echoing in his head. In a day, his empire had gone from being undefeated for a whole millennium—in fact, undefeated since its inception—to the current humiliation.

Meanwhile, in Muruga's camp, news came from Veeramartanda.

Dwitiya

As soon as the next day dawned, Banugopan was ready for battle. It was do or die for him. Agnimukha was not ready yet. He was still engaged in propitiating his goddess. Asurendran was ready and eager to reverse the losses. He was clear about one thing: he was done running away from the enemy. If he was going to be killed in the battlefield, it was going to be that day.

Banugopan and Asurendran came into the courtroom to take

leave from their king. He was nowhere to be found. Amoghan was waiting there. When they asked Amoghan where their father was, he said that the emperor had not come yet, which was unusual. They heard the Kombu and Murasu outside and it threw them off balance. They were not supposed to sound until Banugopan had come out and addressed his army with plans for the day.

Asurendran and Banugopan ran outside and were startled and awestruck by what they saw. Surapadma, in full armour, shining bright in the rising sunlight, stood like a valiant Asura destined for victory. The mere sight of him in that form would strike terror in the hearts of the enemy. Banugopan took his time but the realization that he had been sidelined slowly dawned on him. If the retreat from yesterday's battle plunged him into shame, the fact that his own father doubted his ability now and decided to step in in his place burned him from the inside. He threw his sword down and stormed back to his quarters.

With Surapadma, standing by his side, was Atisuran. Atisuran had been left behind by Simhamukha to help his uncle with the battle. Atisuran admired his uncle even more than his devout father. He also coveted his uncle's throne, seeking to take Banugopan's place. After Banugopan's defeat, Atisuran was eager to impress his uncle, to show him that he was more worthy a successor than Banugopan. Atisuran had promised to destroy Veerabahu while Surapadma would be busy with Muruga. Asurendran meekly joined them for the day's battle.

Surapadma did not care for much strategy, for he felt that his enemy was not worth it. Unlike the previous day's battle, which had been one of strategy and mind games, this was to be a battle of power, strength and sheer will. The news that Surapadma himself would be coming to battle reached Muruga's camp through their spies and Muruga himself got ready for battle that day. Muruga's camp rejoiced more than Sura's, for they believed that this would be the day the war would be over.

Muruga predicted accurately that Sura would not have built a strategy and asked the Veera brothers to go in for brute force. He wanted to demonstrate to Sura that they were superior in strength and power as well, thereby breaking the confidence of Sura who believed that Tarakasura's death and his son's defeat were wrought by strategy and not strength.

Veeramartanda was also back with his newly formed warrior divisions, which comprised of people of all races. They were the ones who hated Asuras so much that their lives did not matter if they could even maim a single Asura. Among them was one of note, whom Veeramartanda had appointed commander, a Bhoota named Ugran. All he wanted to do was kill as many Asuras as possible. He was also a student of Agastya and a devotee of Muruga. Neither of the two forces cared for their lives. They came with only one goal: complete annihilation of the opposition.

The two forces stood opposite one another, standing in columns and facing each other. They were led by Atisuran and Asurendran on the Asura front, while the eight Veera brothers led from the Ganas' front. Surapadma and Muruga were both far back on their side, each waiting for the other to enter the battlefield. Veerabahu was the first to blink and he gave the signal. Like water gushing out of a broken dam during flood, the Gana forces rushed ahead in full fury. Atisuran and Asurendran too gave the signal to their side, and their army, motivated by the fact that their emperor Sura was behind them, were no less in their rush forward. The two forces collided. Thousand-year-old trees were uprooted and thrown at the enemy. Hillocks were broken and used as weapons. Both sides did extensive damage to each other.

Atisuran rushed towards Veeramartanda but was thrown back and out of his chariot by a hillock falling on him, killing his charioteer and the horses. It had been thrown by Ugran. Atisuran was shocked. He had come expecting sophisticated warfare using divine astras and was faced with brutal power and might. Not one to give up so easily, he took his bow and arrow, charged them with multiple mantras to make them very powerful and shot them one by one at his enemy, Ugran.

Being a disciple of Agastya in magical arts and a staunch devotee of Muruga made him immune, so Ugran simply opened his mouth and swallowed the arrows whole, asking Atisuran for more food, all while killing scores of Asuras with his feet, hands and even breath. Atisuran realized that if he did not finish off this enemy quickly, defeat was imminent. He took out his best weapon, the Narayanastra. It was the highest of the Astras of Vishnu and had killed many great Asuras. It was practically unstoppable.

Ugran knew what was coming for him. He realized that this Astra meant death. Wanting to go with his lord's name in his mouth, as the Astra was about to touch him, he called out 'Muruga'. The Astra moved upward from his throat where it had been aimed with the intention of beheading him, and entered his mouth. Seeing this, the Gana army was elated. Surapadma himself was shocked. The Ganas shouted, 'Vetri Vel! Veera Vel!'

Atisuran was desperate. He had taken his best shot and there was nothing else left to do. All he had left with him was the Pasupatastra. Not wanting to face his uncle as a loser, he took it and aimed it at Ugran's heart. The Astra whizzed through the air towards him. The heat generated by it was unbearable. The Asuras were certain that Atisuran had killed Ugran. Ugran himself was certain he was done for.

Surapadma, however, shook his head.

The Pasupatastra went and almost touched Ugran, who again chanted Muruga's name. The Astra then disappeared and went to its creator. Surapadma's charioteer looked at him quizzically, and Surapadma told him that the Astra will not kill anyone who is unarmed, which is why it is usually aimed at a city with the hope that at least one person there would be armed. Atisuran had aimed it at Ugran, who did not wield any weapon, and hence was spared.

After exhausting all his weapons, Atisuran only had himself. He took his mace and rushed at Ugran with his war cry. Ugran caught the mace and crushed it with his bare hands. He caught Atisuran by his neck, lifted him in the air and tore him into two, putting an end to Simhamukha's progeny. The Asura warriors wailed. The Ganas were jubilant and celebrated.

On the other front, Asurendran was fighting like it was the last day of his life. He was killing Ganas left, right and centre, all the while avoiding the Veera brothers. He wanted to inflict maximum damage on the forces of Muruga. Veerabahu jumped up to the sky and landed hard on Asurendran's chariot, breaking it into pieces and killing his charioteer and horses. Asurendran took a gigantic form and started to trample Gana forces.

Seeing the damage Asurendran was inflicting, Veerabahu decided that he should not waste time. He jumped and soared towards the sky, created a scythe out of thin air, grew in stature and landed hard on Asurendran's shoulder, taking his right hand off. Asurendran picked up the fallen gigantic hand, used it as a weapon and hit Veerabahu so hard that he fell miles away. Veerabahu sat up, prayed to his lord and started running towards him, gaining momentum. Asurendran started spinning his right hand with this left hand, waiting to hit the oncoming Veerabahu with it.

The whole battlefield stopped to watch, waiting to see how this would end. Veerabahu's speed printed his footprints onto the rocks he stepped on, while the Ganas and Asuras near Asurendran were blown away by the spinning of his hand. Just as Veerabahu came close, Asurendran swung his hand towards Veerabahu's chest. Veerabahu ducked under it and went behind Asurendran, who turned back and was welcomed by Veerabahu's scythe which took Asurendan's head completely off. The momentum with which Veerabahu swung the scythe caused Asurendran's head to fly through the air and fall at Surapadma's feet.

Veerabahu looked at Sura and shouted, 'Sura! Your head is next!'

The Asura forces ran towards Surapadma, both their commanders having been slain in the battlefield. Surapadma immediately nodded to his charioteer, asking him to take him into the battlefield. As soon as Surapadma entered the war zone, the Asura forces cheered and let out a loud war cry. They were rejuvenated. They were now sure of their victory.

Surapadma took his bow and before anyone could even blink, shot a thousand arrows. They were not regular arrows, but were made from the collected blood of Devas, making them very powerful. Not one of the arrows missed its mark with Surapadma, killing thousands of the Gana forces. Ugran rushed towards Surapadma but was welcomed with a thousand arrows. Made from the blood of Devas and powered by the massive arms and shoulders of Sura, they pierced Ugran, throwing him into the air. While falling down, Ugran made sure that he fell on the Asura forces, killing hundreds of them even with his last breath.

At the sight of Ugran's death, the Asura forces felt even more empowered and launched a full and violent offence on the Ganas and Devas. Seeing his commander Ugran dead, Veeramartanda rushed towards Surapadma. He asked his charioteer to run circles around Surapadma and moved at lightning speed. He shot hundreds of arrows towards Surapadma from all directions. The motion of the chariot raised so much dust that there was no visibility.

Veeramartanda then asked his charioteer to stop to see if he had killed Surapadma. The dust settled. Surapadma was standing in the middle. His chariot, charioteer and his horses were there too. Not a single arrow had touched any of them. All the arrows were countered by Surapadma in spite of the dust cover and they had fallen around Surapadma's chariot, forming a circular wall.

'You are not worthy of fighting me. Where is your lord?' asked Surapadma mockingly.

Veeraratchasa ran full force towards him with a spear in his hands. Surapadma did not even flinch. Just as the spear was about touch him, he simply pushed its head down towards the earth. The spear got planted and the momentum propelled Veeraratchasa towards Veeramartanda. They collided and the impact broke Veeramartanda's chariot. Both fainted from the impact of the collision. The Asura forces, trying to seize the opportunity, swarmed the two brothers but were quickly dealt with by the other Veera brothers.

Veerabahu was silently watching the prowess, might and ability of Surapadma. He realized that he too had underestimated Surapadma. He was indeed deserving of all the praise he had received for his abilities. He understood that being the son of Mahadeva and being blessed by Mahadeva were two different things, the latter having the capacity of making one invincible.

He realized that when Mahadeva blessed Muruga that he would be the one finishing off the Asura race, it meant that no one but him would be able to do it. Not one to back away from the battle, he also realized that Muruga would not enter the field, having tasked Veerabahu to lead the forces. The only way Muruga would come in was when Veerabahu was in danger or had lost the front.

'Sura! I am here. I am the one you want. I am the general here,' said Veerabahu.

'You? The messenger? The one who ran away fearing for his life?' asked Surapadma condescendingly.

'Yes. It is me. I came as a messenger and did my job the other day. I have now come as the general and will do my job of taking your life today,' said Veerabahu.

'No one but Mahadeva himself can take my life, for it is his. I want Muruga. I want to end him. Where is he?' asked Surapadma.

'Go through me and you will be worthy of seeing him as an opponent in the battlefield,' said Veerabahu.

'So be it!' said Surapadma.

Veerabahu took his bow and arrow, shooting arrows at lightning pace. Sura countered all of them with his sword, exhibiting his dexterity. Veerabahu escalated the attack, picking up the Yamastra, Agneyastra, Suryastra and Chandrastra, but they all met the same fate. He then took the Narayanastra. The battlefield was eager to see how Surapadma would counter it. The Astra came flaring at him and he stood still. The Astra hit Sura, sending his chariot a few steps backwards but did not kill him as the Ganas had expected.

Veerabahu, having emptied his arsenal, took out the Pasupatastra and shot it at Surapadma, who took an ordinary arrow, whispered something to it and shot it at the Pasupatastra. The two Astras countered each other and came back to the person who had shot it. Having equalled Veerabahu, Surapadma, who was yet to launch a single attack towards Veerabahu, simply said, 'My turn.'

Surapadma launched a flurry of powerful Astras towards Veerabahu, overwhelming him. He killed his charioteer and horses, destroyed his bow, his chariot, his sword and his mace, leaving him sans weapon. He then hit Veerabahu on his chest with a powerful arrow, breaking his armour and making him faint.

Surapadma then shouted, 'Where are you, little boy? Will you come only if I kill this puny messenger of yours?'

He heard the sound of a massive chariot entering the battlefield. It was, after all, Mahavishnu's. It was helmed by Indra and was pulled by a thousand horses, yet moving at lightning speed; it stopped in front of Surapadma.

Surapadma and Muruga were finally face to face at the final hour of the day.

The Veera brothers carried Veerabahu to safety. Upon seeing their lord, the god of war and victory, enter the battlefield, the Gana forces were rejuvenated and charged at the Asura forces shouting, 'Vetri Vel, Veera Vel!'

'Sura! Your courage and prowess as a warrior are unparalleled, as is your devotion to my father. You can go back and continue to rule the multiverse. Surrender to me, release the Devas and treat them fairly. Redeem yourself. I am not like the ones you have met so far in your existence. I am the son of Shiva. I am here to end you. As much as I do not want to kill a devotee of my father, I would not hesitate to complete the purpose of my coming. You still have time. Reform, repent,' said Muruga.

'Muruga! I say the same to you. You are too young to fight a war, let alone die in one. You are the son of my lord. That was the only reason I spared your generals. Surrender to me and I will not only spare your lives but let you leave and live in peace, unlike the Devas.

'Krauncha was a mere demon. Tarakasura was a coward who got everything only because he was my brother. Killing them and facing me are not the same. Apologize and leave. You still have time. What I do to the Devas is none of your business,' said Surapadma.

'Neither of us is going to budge. You guided by your fate and I guided by my destiny have come to this point. Let us commence the war,' said Muruga as he took his bow and shot an arrow towards Surapadma's chariot.

Surapadma's chariot had been part of thousands of wars and was considered an impregnable fortress by itself. The single ordinary arrow shot by Muruga shattered Surapadma's chariot into smithereens, causing Surapadma and his charioteer to fall to the earth.

The Asura forces and Surapadma himself were shocked. Shame engulfed Surapadma for having fallen off the chariot and to the ground.

Surapadma quickly took an arrow from his quiver and loaded his bow, but before he could shoot it, an ordinary arrow hit his bow and broke it into millions of pieces. The same thing happened with all of the weapons Surapadma tried to wield. Having realized that gross underestimation had led him to under-prepare for his opponent, Surapadma, using his Maya, disappeared into thin air, reappearing at his palace.

Seeing their eminent king Surapadma disappear, the Asura

forces were demoralized and started to run back towards Veeramahendrapuri. Muruga ordered his forces to leave them, for the sun was setting and the war for the day was done.

Surapadma was broken. Mahadeva had blessed him saying that only his power was capable of defeating him. Veerabahu had warned Surapadma that Muruga was no ordinary boy but an incarnate of Mahadeva himself. Was it true? Was his end near? He was bombarded with thousands of thoughts.

In Muruga's camp, Veerabahu and his brothers were recuperating. Muruga came in to see Veerabahu. Upon seeing that they were recovering, Muruga said, 'My brothers, we have shown the Asura that we are superior in strategy. We have shown the Asura that we are superior in might.

'I know you are wondering why I did not finish off Surapadma today. I spared Sura today for he should have time to reflect that he is neither invincible nor immortal. The thoughts might lead to reformation. Surapadma will not come to the battlefield tomorrow. He will need time to regroup and plan, if he is not going to repent and reform. In any case, it will be Banugopan's turn to lead the army. Veerabahu, tomorrow, you will kill Banugopan. That is my order.'

'I will slay Banugopan tomorrow, reminding Surapadma that his death is imminent, as you ordered, my lord!' said Veerabahu. Muruga left them to rest.

Surapadma was on his throne, all by himself. He had dismissed Amoghan for the day. He then left for Banugopan's quarters.

Banugopan was seething with anger. 'Permission to speak, my emperor,' Banugopan said formally.

'Speak, my son,' said Sura.

'What you did was despicable, Father! Neither did you consult me, nor did you inform me. Having appointed me as the general, it was your duty to take me into confidence. You should have at least confided in me to get inputs as to how powerful our enemies are.

'You going to the battlefront without talking to me clearly shows that you are ashamed of me for having lost. Besides, there is no shame in me losing to Muruga, for I am not as battle worn as you are. You losing to him has permanently sullied the name of the Asura clan. You should have waited till my death to enter the battlefield. You should have waited till Uncle's return. Even if you had defeated Muruga today, like Uncle said, people would have laughed, saying that it required your presence to defeat a mere boy. I will enter the battlefield tomorrow. I will bring Muruga bound hand and feet to you, using Maya,' said Banugopan.

'No, my son. You will not be able to defeat Muruga. Go for Veerabahu. I want him bound hand and feets. We will use him to negotiate,' said Surapadma.

Banugopan vowed to do so.

Surapadma left Banugopan's quarters to go to his own. Tired from the battle and relaxed at the thought of his son accomplishing the conceivable, he slept in peace.

Banugopan went to meet his mother, took her blessings and returned to his quarter. Back in his room, he sat down and called out his grandmother, Surasai, in his head. No sooner than he called her out, she appeared in front of him.

'What do you want my child? Did you think of me?' asked Surasai.

'Yes, Grandmother. The situation is not good. We are in the middle of a war. We have underestimated the enemy. I went...' said Banugopan, but he was stopped by Surasai.

'I know, my dear child. I saw everything. You have something on your mind, ask for it and I shall give it to you,' she said.

'Please give me an Astra capable of binding Veerabahu. Our plan is to capture him and use him to negotiate an end to the war and thereby gain victory over the enemy,' said Banugopan.

'Here, this is Sammohanastra. This is capable of not only binding the person you have in mind, but also his entire army.

Unlike the Mohanastra, this will not be cancelled out by the Amohanastra,' said Surasai as she handed it over to him.

Banugopan thanked his grandmother and went to sleep.

Surasai, meanwhile, being a staunch devotee of Mahadeva, had already realized that the end was near for her clan. It was one of the reasons why she took the three children of Tarakasura with her for the purpose of tutoring them. She knew that Banugopan was going to fail and also knew that Surapadma would never surrender or compromise, which would lead to the total annihilation of her progeny. She lamented that her sons' unbending nature, which had led to their rise, would also lead to their fall, with their race's highs and lows tied to them. She still blessed her grandson wholeheartedly, praying to the supreme Mahadeva for his Moksha.

Banugopan slept in peace with a plan in place for the next day. He was going after Veerabahu and no one else.

Veerabahu's mind was also completely occupied with the thought of Banugopan, whom he was going to kill the next day, as ordered by his lord.

Tritiya

$\mathcal{B}$anugopan could not hold back his anxiety, excitement and dread as he woke up the next day. He was anxious to see how well the new Astra would work, excited to redeem his name in the battlefield and dreaded the thought of returning a loser. He had done his homework and collected all the details of the events that had transpired the previous day. The exhibition of brute force that took the life of his brothers, Asurendran and Atisuran, made it abundantly clear to Banugopan that his enemies were not only stronger in terms of Astras and strategy but also in brute strength. He would have to use his Maya to overcome and accomplish the task he had set for the day.

He wore full armour and went to the courtroom. For the first time, his father was standing and waiting for him proudly, and hugged him.

'Banugopan, my son, the valiant one who squashed the rebellion in the Surya empire! Go forth and complete the task that you have taken upon yourself. Do not waste a single moment and do not engage Muruga. Go after Veerabahu. Use deceit, use Maya, use everything you have at your disposal. You have my complete and wholehearted blessings,' said Surapadma.

'Your orders will be executed even at the cost of my life, Father. I will come back with Veerabahu,' said Banugopan, not even entertaining the thought of coming back without Veerabahu or not coming back at all.

He then met his wife and bade her farewell, saying, 'Tonight, when I come back, I will come back to a hero's welcome, unlike last time. You will be proud of being my wife, the valiant Asura, the heir to the Asura empire, Banugopan.'

He then turned to Amoghan, who had been a teacher and mentor, in addition to his role as a minister and said, 'Bless me as my teacher, Amoghan.'

Amoghan said, 'May victory be yours. Remember, all is fair in war. There is no worse shame in war than being a loser. You can do anything to win a war and once you have won, you will always be heralded a hero, irrespective of how you won it.'

Banugopan left to meet his forces; He addressed them and gave them specific instructions, especially to the handpicked ones adept at Maya, to keep the other brothers at bay and away from him, even at the cost of their lives, while he went after Veerabahu.

Veerabahu, meanwhile, before setting out to war, sought an audience with Muruga, who said, 'I know why you are here, my general. You have my blessings and complete backing. Do not hold back. The enemy has seen our strategy, he has seen our might. He will use guile and tricks. He will use Maya. Do not compete with him in that. Our father's order is to fight the war fairly. We will do so. If you are in trouble, remember, I am always there. There is no fear when I am here.'

Veerabahu prostrated himself before Muruga and said, 'I will come back with the news of Banugopan's death, my lord,' and left.

The two massive forces stood before each other. On the first day, the Asura army had been outdone in strategy and Astras and on the second day, they had been outdone in brute force. Now, they were demoralized even more, seeing that they were not to be led by Surapadma, who was the only one who had shown some promise against the Veera brothers. They did not doubt the efficacy of Banugopan as a general, but were more worried for him and his well-being. The Ganas, on the other hand, were upbeat and riding high on their emphatic victory over the Asura forces over the last two days. They chanted their war cry, drowning that of the Asura forces.

Veerabahu and Banugopan had their eyes fixed on each other. After all, they were each other's target for the day. The only difference was that one wanted the other's life and the other knew that he would not be able to take his opponent's life, wishing only to take his freedom, by any and all means possible. The two forces were waiting for the command from their respective leaders.

Banugopan gave the command, as did Veerabahu, and the forces collided. The marked men in the Asura army went right after their target, the Veera brothers. Veerabahu and Banugopan were stationary, each waiting for the other to move.

'Fight, you coward! Or are you going to run away today as well?' asked Veerabahu to Banugopan, who did not even flinch.

'I hate to kill someone who is not fighting, but you are in the battlefield. You are an enemy and you have all the weapons at your disposal and I have neither the time nor the patience to wait to take your life,' said Veerabahu as he launched an arrow towards Banugopan.

Banugopan remained motionless and the arrow went straight towards his chest. It went through him and came out behind him. Banugopan laughed loudly as it did not even scratch him. Veerabahu was first confused, but it became clear that Banugopan was playing games. Veerabahu had only heard of those who wielded Maya, but had never met one who practiced it so well. He had thought that the stories were exaggerated, but for the first time, he was experiencing the force, that too in adverse conditions.

An arrow came from the left and took out Veerabahu's chariot wheels and his chariot listed on one side. Veerabahu turned and saw one more Banugopan on that side, while the Banugopan in front of him was still laughing. He quickly turned to his right and saw a Banugopan there as well. He turned back and there was one more Banugopan. All of them were armed with bows and arrows, ready to fire. All of them released their arrows at the exact same moment.

Not sure which one was the true arrow, Veerabahu jumped towards the sky and all four arrows shattered his chariot, killing his horses and wounding his charioteer. All four Banugopans laughed. The Asuras cheered and the Ganas were worried. The Veera brothers tried to come to their brother's aide, but were engaged by equally adept Maya wielders.

Veerabahu landed. He was not sure which one of the four he was to go after. He prayed to Muruga and jumped up into the sky and one more Banugopan appeared above him. Unfortunately, he took this Banugopan for an illusion, though this was the real one. He kicked Veerabahu on his chest, sending him crashing to the ground. The Asura army cheered even louder. They were elated to see the display of Maya live on the battlefield.

Veerabahu understood what Banugopan was doing. He had created shells of himself in four directions and was switching the shell with his real self so quickly and adeptly that no one could notice the switch. The shells, by themselves, were hollow, but with

Banugopan's efficiency in switching, no matter which one Veerabahu went after, it would be the wrong one.

Veerabahu had to think of something and think of it quickly. He picked the one to the left and rushed at him with full force. The Asura forces were sure that Veerabahu would be thrown hard to the ground again. Just as he was about to connect, he turned one hundred and eighty degrees and gave a resounding kick using his full might and power, shouting 'Vetri Vel, Veera Vel!'

His kick connected. Banugopan had taken the shell of the one on the right, using it to attack Veerabahu from behind, as Veerabahu had predicted.

The kick threw Banugopan across the battlefield. He fell hard and was hurt by the power of Veerabahu. Banugopan realized how well his brother Vajrabahu must have fought against Veerabahu, so much so that Veerabahu had left a flower as a sign of respect for him.

The Gana army cheered loudly and were rejuvenated in their attack against the Asura army.

Not wanting to waste any more time, the fallen Banugopan soared into the sky. Veerabahu lunged after him into the air as well. As he was about catch the leg of Banugopan, an arrow came from below and hit Veerabahu. It was the Sammohanastra.

Veerabahu simply had the time to look down and see a jubilant Banugopan laughing at him from below, along with the other four Banugopans, while the one above him turned out to be a mere shell. The Astra bound him and rendered him unconscious. Banugopan immediately switched to the shell above Veerabahu, landed on his chest and came down crashing with his falling body. The Astra with the power to bind a whole army was targeted on the single personage of Veerabahu.

Banugopan, for a moment, believed, hoped, that he had killed Veerabahu. He realized very quickly that it took a lot more to kill someone as powerful as Veerabahu, the son of Shiva and Shakti, carrying the grace and blessings of both.

Meanwhile, Veeramartanda somehow managed to break free of his opponent and shot his Amohanastra, since he was the only one, other than Veerabahu and the lord himself, capable of using it. As his attention was turned towards Veerabahu, as soon as he shot the arrow, he was attacked from behind by his opponent, rendering him unconscious as well.

The Ganas were shocked to see that not only had Veerabahu and Veeramartanda fallen, but the Amohanastra did not work either. Banugopan then shot the Mohanastra at Veerakesari, who was now in command after Veerabahu was rendered unconscious. With that, the entire Gana army were bound and fell unconscious.

The Asura army stood tall in the middle of the battlefield with the Gana army and its generals unconscious. They were jubilant, as if they have won the war. Banugopan was elated that he had completed his plan and executed it well. He placed Veerabahu on his shoulders, preparing to leave the battlefield while the rest of the Asura army could massacre the immobile, unconscious Gana army. If only he had realized that the enemy's general was still present and, he, unlike any other opponent that Banugopan had faced, was invincible.

The whole battlefield became illuminated as if it was dawn, as Muruga's chariot arrived. The Asuras could not take their eyes off him. All the shells of Banugopan and his elite disappeared at the mere appearance of the radiance of Muruga. They were spellbound.

Muruga took his Vel and threw it across the battlefield. It circled the battlefield and wherever it crossed the unconscious Ganas, Devas and Veeras, they not only regained their senses but also became even more invigorated. The Vel moved towards Veerabahu on Banugopan's shoulder, brushing against him and waking him up instantaneously. Banugopan could not even move a muscle against it. The Vel then went back to Muruga, who left the battlefield, leaving Veerabahu to his devices.

Banugopan felt pangs of anger, not because Muruga had to come in and spoil his plan, but because he had been left untouched. Unlike his father, he was not even afforded a chance to face Muruga. 'Am I not worthy enough?' wondered Banugopan.

Veerabahu caught Banugopan's hips while on his shoulder, threw himself off and used the momentum of his fall to reverse their positions. Banugopan was now sitting on Veerabahu's shoulders with his legs around his neck, as Veerabahu slammed him hard against the earth, waking him up to reality.

The Veera brothers went after their dazed opponents, making short work of them while the Gana army went after the Asura army.

Veerabahu soared into the sky, increasing in size as he went higher and higher. He stopped for a moment, called out to his lord from the depth of his heart and went straight down. The sound generated by Veerabahu's descent, tearing through the air, deafened everyone in the battlefield. Both the armies stood spellbound, watching how this would pan out.

Veerabahu landed squarely on Banugopan's chest, right over his heart, pushing Banugopan into the earth with pure power and sheer force, coupled with the momentum gained from to his rapid descent. He then bounced off Banugopan's chest and landed with his back towards Banugopan.

Veerabahu turned around to see if Banugopan was dead: his body had left a massive imprint on the ground, complete with broad shoulders and a wide chest. Veerabahu shouted, 'Vetri Vel!' and the whole Gana army responded with a thundering, 'Veera Vel!'

With Banugopan and his elite soldiers dead, the Asura army had no one to lead them. Veerabahu addressed the Asura army: 'Take your brave general and prince. He fought valiantly and fearlessly. But for my lord's grace, he would have not only won this battle but the war as well. He is a true hero and an unparalleled warrior and he has earned my utmost respect.' He bowed to Banugopan and, seeing him, the Gana army did the same as well.

Veerabahu dug into the earth to take out Banugopan's body. The Veera brothers joined him and lifted the lifeless body, which had a deep imprint of Veerabahu's feet on the chest. Veerabahu placed Banugopan's body in his chariot and asked his charioteer to take him to his kingdom and to inform the emperor how heroically Banugopan fought and how he had almost won the battle.

The Asura palace was fully prepared to celebrate and welcome Banugopan in a grand manner, for they were sure of his victory in his mission. Surapadma was pacing to and fro. Amoghan was the first to rush in, tears were rolling down his cheeks. He threw himself down in front of his emperor.

'The prince is dead,' said Amoghan as he burst into wails.

Surapadma sank down on his throne. His wife and Banugopan's wife came running out at the news of Banugopan's death, something they had never thought they would see, for he was as valiant as they came, without the gift of boon from Mahadeva. Banugopan's wife fainted at the sight of his dead body, never to wake up again.

'How!' asked Surapadma to Amoghan.

'He fought valiantly, my lord. The soldiers said that for a moment, they were not sure if they were seeing Banugopan or Surapadma in the battlefield. He wielded Maya so well and used his Astras so efficiently that he not only caught Veerabahu but had the entire Gana army unconscious at one point. They genuinely believed that they had won.

'Then, Muruga came in. He threw his Vel, which set the Gana army free from Banugopan's Astra and reinvigorated Veerabahu, who then killed Banugopan in the same way that he had killed Vajrabahu,' said Amoghan.

'Veerabahu! Your life will end only at my hands,' thundered Surapadma in pain and wrath.

'Your honour, there is more,' said Amoghan. Surapadma looked at him quizzically. Amoghan continued, 'Veerabahu and his brothers then gave a eulogy praising Banugopan. He went on to acknowledge the fact that but for the interference of Muruga, he would have been beaten that day by Banugopan. He called him the bravest and most valiant warrior he had ever met. They all bowed to him, lifted him from the earth, placed him on the chariot, paid their respects and sent him off to us. He also told our soldiers to celebrate the life of such a legendary warrior.'

Surapadma was battered by conflicting emotions: hatred for Veerabahu and respect for his magnanimity. 'What greater honour can a warrior have than the praise of an enemy?' Surapadma consoled himself, and asked Amoghan to arrange for a grand funeral to celebrate the life of Banugopan. He then summoned his two sons, Iranian and Agnimukha. He said that they would be taking to the battlefield the next day.

Iranian objected, saying, 'Father! Do you not see? The person has come here by the grace of Mahadeva. He is the son of Mahadeva, the very Mahadeva who made you invincible, except for his power. We have lost our uncles Tarakasura and Krauncha. We have lost my cousins Asurendran and Atisuran. We have lost our invincible and undefeated elder brother Banugopan. How many more lives does your pride seek to satiate itself?'

'Shut up, you coward!' shouted Agnimukha. 'Our lives have been given to us by the grace of our father. He has every right to ask for it, even if he knows our death is certain. Does your blood not boil? Does pure Asura blood not run in your veins? Are you truly the son of the scion of Asuras? Our esteemed and beloved brother has just been murdered. Do you not seek vengeance? Are you even a man? Father! I will go tomorrow, even if I am all alone. I will come back with the head of that Veerabahu who killed my brother, or I will not come back at all,' said Agnimukha.

Surapadma's eyes turned to Iranian.

'As you order, my father. I shall do the duty of a son to his father and that of a brother to his brother. I will go and fight with all my heart. I go with only one hope: let our deaths be the last in the Asura clan and, with our deaths, may you see the light,' said Iranian as he left.

In Muruga's camp, the Veera brothers met with Muruga, who blessed them, saying that they had done very well. Veerabahu hesitantly asked Muruga if Surapadma would be coming the next day, so that they can finish off this war. Muruga said that neither did he expect Surapadma to come until all the Asuras were done for, nor did he expect Surapadma to reform himself.

The Veera brothers left as Muruga summoned Veerabahu alone, as his brother and not as the general.

'Tomorrow will be a test for your courage, Veerabahu. Have no fear. Even an iota of fear will be your downfall. Remember, there is no fear when I am here,' said Muruga cryptically, as he pointed towards Veerabahu's chest.

'Yes, my brother. Why fear when you are here,' Veerabahu repeated as he left to take rest and prepare for another round of large-scale massacre of lives, for the pride of a man who refused to acknowledge that his end was near and that he was in the wrong with his actions towards his own stepbrothers. 'If the death of one's own beloved sons cannot reform such a man, there is no reforming him,' thought Veerabahu.

They all went to sleep in peace and Agnimukha went to pray.

Chaturthi

*W*ithout a wink of sleep, Agnimukha walked out aggressively from his quarters the next morning, after spending the entire night propitiating his goddess, Bhadrakali. Iranian too walked out, but unlike Agnimukha, he was not full of arrogance; instead, he was resigned to his fate.

Surapadma was sitting on his throne, his eyes red from the

lack of sleep and crying for his dead son, Banugopan. His son and daughter-in-law went together, consumed by fire in the pyre. He had completed the funeral, came back, sat here and had not budged since. He was holding on to his place like he was holding on to his position of power. Amoghan brought him food which he refused. He also refused to sleep.

Agnimukha and Iranian bowed to their father and said that they were going to battle. Surapadma was motionless. Amoghan told them that he had been like that the whole night immersed in sorrow and despair. Both bade farewell to their father and left to address the assembled army.

Agnimukha, who was the general now, spoke: 'My fellow Asuras, you all saw how close we were to victory yesterday. If Muruga had not come, we would have won. Today, we shall go out and fight. We shall fight for the honour of the Asura race. We shall go out and fight to reclaim our emperor's right as the ruler of the multiverse. Above all, we shall go out and fight to avenge our slain prince, the general with unassailable prowess, the unparalleled warrior, Banugopan.'

As soon as his name was mentioned, the Asura army let out their war cry in unison. Then, they all marched out to the battlefield.

'Can I ask you something, Brother?' asked Iranian. 'How do you think you will fare against Veerabahu, let alone Muruga? Do you not see that they have beaten not only our brother but even our father? Do you not remember that you were among those who were beaten on the first day?'

'Neither am I an idiot nor am I rushing into the battle headlong, propelled by my emotions. I know what I am doing. You are my brother. Fight hard. Spare none. We have lost Banugopan. We should take the life of at least one of the Veera brothers today. I will take on Veerabahu. Don't go near Veerakesari, Veeramartanda or Veerandhaka. I have faced them and seen them in battle. You will not be able to bear them. Go after any of the other Veera brothers and slay them. Let our enemy feel the pain we felt at the death of our beloved elder brother, Banugopan,' said Agnimukha.

'I will do as you say, my brother,' said Iranian, fully realizing that his efforts were going to be futile.

In the battlefield, the two armies stood face to face. Without Surapadma, the Gana army realized that this was going to be one more day in the war and not the final one. Veerabahu signalled his army to go forth and they rushed at the enemy. Agnimukha wasted no time giving the signal to his forces. The two forces collided.

Veerabahu and Agnimukha directed their chariots towards each other. Just as they reached within striking distance of each other, a gruesome form ripped apart the earth and emerged. It was Bhadrakali. This was the second time that she had come to battle, after she came to aid Veerabhadra during the Daksha yagna.

Seeing the striking form of Bhadrakali, the horses tore away from Veerabahu's chariot and ran away. His charioteer, a Deva, fainted, remembering the events of Daksha's yagna. The Asura army cheered and celebrated, even though they were terrified of her form. The Ganas trembled at the sight of her as she stood like a giant, weapons adorning her eight hands.

Only two people stood fearlessly in the battlefield: Agnimukha, who through his sacrifices and prayer had propitiated her and summoned her to help him in this battle, and Veerabahu, who remembered what his lord had told him. He stared chanting his lord's name in his heart and stood courageously in front of her.

The Gana army looked at Veerabahu, waiting to see if he was going to order a retreat. Veerabahu put his weapon down, folded his hands and worshipped Bhadrakali. He recognized her as an aspect of his mother, Shakti. Bhadrakali smiled. She blessed him as she said, 'Who are you? I can feel some familiarity with you but am not sure who you are.'

'Mother Bhadrakali, I am the son of Mahadeva and Parvati, who is Shakti incarnate. I am the general of the Gana army, led by

Muruga, son of Mahadeva and Parvati as well. We are fighting the war to re-establish Dharma and free the Devas who are enduring unspeakable acts of torture at the hands of the Asuras, led by Surapadma and his clan. Kindly bless me and give me permission to carry on with the war,' replied Veerabahu humbly.

'You know who I am and whose side I am on, yet you seek to battle with me. I admire your courage and sense of duty. You have my permission as well as my blessings. I will battle for Agnimukha so long as the merits he gained through his sacrifices hold good, even though you are my son,' said Bhadrakali.

Having gained permission, Veerabahu took to his weapons. He started with his standard arrows and they were met with absolute disdain from Bhadrakali. Meanwhile, seeing Veerabahu stand up to and fight Bhadrakali, the Gana army was motivated and started to fight the Asura army. Iranian went after Veerakendra.

Veerabahu then took out the Mahagneyastra and shot it at Bhadrakali, who opened her mouth and swallowed all the flames that came out of the Astra, along with the Astra itself, which scorched the earth, killing everyone it is path.

Bhadrakali then flung her scimitar at Veerabahu, who created a scythe by worshipping Muruga, which he used to block the scimitar. The force with which the two blades met threw Veerabahu to the ground. He stood up again and, this time, he used the Vayuastra. This caused a huge hurricane in the middle of the battlefield, which again took thousands of lives along its path as it went towards Bhadrakali. Predictably, this was no match for someone as powerful as her, even though she was in a mellow form. She sucked in the air around the hurricane, causing it to die down.

Veerabahu then shot the Vajrastra of Indra. It struck Bhadrakali with bolts of lightning, but she caught the Vajrastra with her bare hands and broke it into two. The Narayanastra and even the Pasupatastra met with the same fate. Bhadrakali then launched her trident at Veerabahu. He stood before it fearlessly, clasping his hands and bowing before it, accepting his fate as he chanted his lord's name. The Vel, thrown by Muruga, intercepted the trident and made both weapons return to their owners. Bhadrakali recognized the Vel for what it was.

Bhadrakali was pleased. She smiled at Veerabahu, admiring not only his courage and bravery but also his relentlessness in attacking her, even though he knew the futility of it. She also appreciated his devotion to his brother and lord, Muruga.

She turned to Agnimukha and said, 'Son, I have fought your battle for you. The merits you gained by your sacrifices were exhausted the moment I swallowed the Pasupatastra. I threw the trident to finish off your enemy, as reward for your devotion, even though your devotion had an ulterior motive. Veerabahu's devotion to his lord is selfless and his lord came and saved him even without being asked. He wavered not in his devotion even for a moment. I have done all that I am expected to do for what you gave me. My duty here is finished, you are on your own.'

Bhadrakali then blessed Veerabahu and disappeared from the battlefield. The Gana army cheered.

At the other end of the battlefield, Veerakendra and Iranian were fighting hard. As hesitant as Iranian had been before the battle, once he stepped in and started to fight, he was a different beast. He efficiently used a combination of Maya, knowledge of Astras and training in war strategies, making it extremely difficult for Veerakendra to get rid of him. However, in spite of trying his best, he could not finish off Veerakendra.

At one point, Veerakendra started to outmatch the Astras and see through Iranian's Maya. To escape the onslaught, Iranian turned into a fish and jumped into the ocean surrounding them. Veerakendra shot an Agneyastra into the ocean, causing the water to evaporate. Samudra ran to Iranian and asked him to leave the ocean, for he was a neutral party in the war and did not want his subjects, the sea life, to suffer. The kind Iranian understood the position of Samudra and returned to the battlefield. Veerakendra withdrew the Agneyastra and restored the ocean.

Veerakendra and Iranian rushed at each other and fought hard with maces, scimitars, trees and rocks. Veerakendra, however, outmatched Iranian in strength and stamina. Finally, Veerakendra lifted his opponent high up in the sky and threw him hard to the ground. Iranian fell on a protruding rock, which went through his heart, killing him. Iranian died with a smile, saying Mahadeva's name. Veerakendra bowed to him and prayed to Mahadeva, seeking clemency for killing his ardent devotee.

After Bhadrakali's departure, Agnimukha stood in front of Veerabahu. He knew that his Astras were useless. He knew his Maya, not as efficient as Banugopan's or even Iranian's, was also useless. His sacrifices and prayers had been exhausted, for he depended too much on Bhadrakali, instead of doing his part at the beginning. Had he weakened Veerabahu initially and then summoned Bhadrakali, her attack on him would have killed him. Instead, he had entirely depended on her instead of believing in himself and fighting. He felt betrayed, though reason told him that he had merely made a business deal with Bhadrakali for favours and was not a true devotee.

All that was left to be done was to attack Veerabahu. Agnimukha rushed at him with his scimitar. Veerabahu created a scimitar, worshipping his lord, and the two scimitars met each other, sending out a clang that shook the battlefield. They fought long with the scimitars but that was only because Veerabahu had been weakened by the battle with Bhadrakali.

At one point, Agnimukha even tried a low blow, but Veerabahu avoided it cleverly. Agnimukha was losing his energy, patience and hope. In his final rush, he mustered all his strength and hit Veerabahu. The latter was able to use his momentum and reflex in his favour and spun his scimitar to take off Agnimukha's head in one clean sweep. The head flew and landed in the middle of battlefield.

The Asura army was now without a leader in the battlefield, but Veerabahu did not instruct the Gana army to stop. As the Asura army tried to retreat and scramble back to Veeramahendrapuri, the Gana army ransacked them. Whoever could run fast saved themselves. The Asuras were met by Amoghan's officers once they were safely inside. He quickly got an update from them and rushed to inform Surapadma of the fate of his last two sons. The entire Asura lineage, except Surapadma, Simhamukha, Ajamukhi and the three children of Tarakasura, had been erased.

Surapadma still did not move. He sat motionless, in shock. Amoghan was worried for him and even got the queen, Padumakomalai, who was more upset and worried about the state of her husband than the death of all her children. She hugged his feet and wailed, begging him to wake up, but he remained motionless and emotionless. The sight of his empire, his children, his army being massacred right in front of him, while he was unable to do anything, was something he could not digest, for he had never anticipated such a day.

'Brother,' a kind voice called.

Surapadma immediately roused himself and ran towards Simhamukha. He hugged him as he cried, for Banugopan, Agnimukha, Iranian and the scores of others who had been killed. Simhamukha, however, did not cry.

'I am sorry, Simhamukha. Your son, Atisuran, is dead too,' said Surapadma.

'Death is imminent for one and all. Everyone who is born has to die. My son died a warrior in a battlefield, falling to a better enemy, a divine enemy. I am glad that he got that honour,' philosophized the mature Kali devotee, Simhamukha. 'We should talk about the living now. I am here, Brother. I am here with my army. You still have time. Whatever I told you then, whatever Amoghan would have told you every day, still holds good. We still can redeem ourselves. Reform, repent, change. Let us seek mercy from the sons of Shiva. Let us free the Devas. You will continue to rule the multiverse, my brother,' said Simhamukha.

Surapadma was enraged by his brother's words.

'Stop speaking like a coward! You are a better warrior than me. I use more Maya than might to fight but you are more powerful than me. You have beaten me and Taraka in all our fights to see which of us is the strongest. It pains me to hear you talk like a coward when I look to you as my last and only hope. Surapadma will rather be dead than the ruler of the multiverse through the mercy of an enemy,' said Sura.

'I knew that this is what you would say, Brother. Tomorrow, I shall go to battle. I do not know if I will return or not, for it is Kali's will. But I do say this, if I die in the battlefield, seek peace with Muruga, surrender and save yourself. Save our clan,' said Simhamukha as he left to take rest and prepare for the next day's battle.

Meanwhile, Muruga's camp was eager, for they were hoping that Surapadma would finally appear the next day and the war would be over. The Nava Veeras and Muruga were in consultation.

Muruga said, 'You all did well. The time is nearing. Have patience and courage. All this will soon be over. There is only Surapadma, Ajamukhi and Simhamukha left. I anticipate that Simhamukha will enter the battlefield tomorrow. Fight him with all your might, as you have done until now. I am always there to back you in case you need me.'

Veerabahu replied, 'Yes, my lord. As long as you are there behind us, nothing and no one can touch us.'

Muruga then asked them to go back to their quarters and rest for the night, as the next day was going to be a long one.

Surapadma, however, could not rest. He was pacing to and fro in the courtroom. Amoghan, the wise and intelligent minister, had again been dismissed. He was filled with wrath and vengeance. He was angry at the thought that Mahadeva had forsaken him. 'Had his devotion to Mahadeva not been enough?' he asked himself. Are the boons he got from the supreme lord himself bound to fail? Was he not worthy of being the emperor of the multiverse any more in the eyes of Mahadeva? He wanted to go to Kailash and confront his god. Unfortunately, he also realized that he did not have the time for it. Instead, he went to the gigantic statue of Mahadeva and fell at its feet, asking for guidance after having shunned guidance wherever and whenever he had received it from sane minds. Eventually, he fell asleep at Mahadeva's feet.

He woke up hours later. It was not dawn yet. He closed his eyes, calmed down and sat in meditation. When he woke up again after a couple of hours, the sun was yet to rise. He had come to a decision. He knew what he was going to do: he realized that it was the best step forward.

Panchami

The sun rose. Simhamukha rose with the sun. He woke up early, spent the first hour of his day worshipping his divine mother and then set out to complete the work planned for the day. To him, whether it was the last day of his life or not, it was just another day, another opportunity his divine mother had given him to worship her, think of her, chant her name and, above all, serve her by performing his duty. His duty for that day was war.

His approach to life was simple. Every single day, he did his duty based on what came to him, taking it as the order of his divine mother, Kali, performing the task to the best of his ability and dedicating the result to her.

Simhamukha stepped out in full splendour, wearing his armour. He was bigger than Surapadma and a sight that one could not look away from easily. He went to the courtroom and met his brother.

He hugged him and took a long look at him. They bade their goodbyes and Simhamukha came and stood before his massive army. Simhamukha was so broad that the shadow of his frame blocked the sun and plunged almost half the army that stood before him in shade. They were ecstatic to see him, having only heard about his valour, courage, prowess, strength and power. They were excited at the mere prospect of seeing him in action.

Simhamukha spoke in a deep baritone: 'Today, we first attack the Gana army while I go after the nine generals. We chase them off. We chase them right into Skandamadana, where I will take on this valiant son of our supreme lord, Mahadeva. Forget what they were capable of yesterday. Forget what they did yesterday or the day before or the day before that. Today is a new day that Kali has given us. I pray to Kali to give us the strength to defeat the enemy and graciousness to accept defeat if we were to fail.'

The Asura army was spellbound by his form and deep leonine voice.

Meanwhile, Muruga was giving instructions to the Nava Kumaras, 'There is no shame in war. I have saved you all once from Surapadma. I saved you all from Banugopan. I have saved you, my brother Veerabahu, from Bhadrakali. I will save you no matter what. If you feel overwhelmed by the opposition, do not hesitate to come back to us. We can always regroup and there is always a tomorrow, as long as we live. We beat them for four days straight and we shall beat them today as well. This war will end with the end of the Asura race, as our father ordered.'

The two armies stood face to face. The Nava Kumaras could not take their eyes off Simhamukha's massive stature. Veerabahu, particularly, was overwhelmed by the thought of fighting someone so magnificent. This was different from facing Surapadma, who was always the intended target. Veerabahu saw him as an enemy. About Simhamukha, on the other hand, he had only heard good things. Having seen him in person, the respect increased manifold.

On the other side, Simhamukha too was impressed by Veerabahu. After all, he had killed many valiant Asuras that he himself had seen fight and had trained. Many of them were considered the best by him. What impressed Simhamukha more was that he could feel Veerabahu's mind constantly dwelling on Muruga's name. He had never felt such utter devotion emanating from any person other than himself.

Both gave the signal at the same time and the two forces went forth. Even before the Nava Kumaras could decide if they should go for Simhamukha, their eight chariots shattered into pieces. They did not even see the arrows that were launched at them. These arrows, unlike the ones used by the other warriors, were unique. Surapadma used red arrows made from the crystallized blood of Devas. Simhamukha's arrows were shining black like his attire.

Even before they could take out their bows, eight more arrows hit the Veeras felling them. Veerabahu was a mute spectator. All this happened even before he could shoot the first arrow at Simhamukha. Unlike Surapadma, Simhamukha's arrows had purpose and went after a specific target, causing only the intended damage. Veerabahu waited for his brothers get up. They did not. He became worried, wondering if they were dead. He turned to Simhamukha, who did not have an arrow mounted on his bow, as if he were waiting to allow Veerabahu to go and check on his brothers.

Veerabahu turned his chariot to his nearest brother and saw that his brother had fainted. The arrow was still lodged, but it had not hit any vital organs. He had fainted from the powerful impact, though the arrow was not a divine Astra. Veerabahu wondered how powerful Simhamukha really was.

The Asura army was jubilant. The Ganas were distraught. The enemy had slain eight of their nine generals within minutes of the start. Veerabahu had to take control of the situation. He ordered his charioteer to escort his brothers back to the base camp, remembering what Muruga said. He then turned to Simhamukha and challenged him.

Simhamukha alighted from his chariot, wanting to be on equal ground with his adversary.

Veerabahu started running towards Simhamukha, who remained still. As he arrived within striking distance, he made a fist to deliver a punch to Simhamukha's face. He anticipated Simhamukha to block the punch or worse, take it unaffected to show off his power.

However, Simhamukha gracefully moved his head back a little, making Veerabahu completely miss his target. With an open hand, he merely nudged Veerabahu, who went flying and fell at the other end of the battlefield.

Veerabahu had never met this kind of power. This was different, someone in complete control, who used minimal movements and went for specific targets. Simhamukha had so much grace. Veerabahu was in awe, not at the power of the nudge from Simhamukha's hands, but his choice of not killing him at that very moment.

Simhamukha understood what Veerabahu was thinking. He said, 'My dear Veerabahu, there is no rivalry between us. I do not want your life. I want this war to end. The only way this war can end is with death, either Surapadma's or Muruga's. I want to fight Muruga. Based on what I have heard, he won't come in unless you are in danger. Forgive me, for I have to kill you for that reason alone.'

Simhamukha then started running towards Veerabahu like a massive lion, living up to his name. He also had the nobility that the name called for. The vibration of his footsteps landing on the earth made shockwaves, as it had done with Tarakasura, except that Tarakasura made the waves using his full potential, while Simhamukha was doing it effortlessly.

Realizing that he was in danger, Veerabahu got up, planted his feet firmly and soared towards the sky, looking down at Simhamukha. He half closed his eyes for a second and the next moment, Simhamukha was not there. Veerabahu could feel breath on his neck. His eyes shifted to the side to see and confirm his worst fear: Simhamukha rising above him. He lightly kicked Veerabahu's back, breaking his ribs and making him cry out in pain as he came crashing down to earth.

The Asura army loudly chanted their war cry in joy, not merely at the sight of their dreaded enemy being slain, but also at the grace with which their king was doing it.

Simhamukha landed near Veerabahu and addressed him: 'Pray to your lord, for the next move I am going to make is aimed to end your life.'

He took a step forward, but the Vel, in all its divine grace and beauty, came whizzing right up to Simhamukha's face and sliced off his head. His body fell to the ground and his head fell far away. The Vel went back to the hand of Muruga, who entered the battlefield. The Gana army cheered, the Asura faces fell. Veerabahu was quickly taken out of the battlefield by the Ganas nearby.

Muruga walked towards Simhamukha's body, which rested in a seated position with the head intact. Every single pair of eyes on the battlefield turned towards the severed head to see if it was still there. Everyone wondered if Simhamukha had used Maya as Banugopan had. No, the severed head was still there. Simhamukha's head had grown back. He had sacrificed his head to Mahadeva to please him, while his brothers had merely given their blood, so Mahadeva had decreed that his head would grow back a thousand times. This was only the first.

Muruga and Simhamukha faced each other. No two people could have been more different. Simhamukha was gigantic and broad shouldered, with a face that resembled a lion and a voice that matched the face. Muruga looked like an ordinary young boy with his single head and one of his two hands carrying a Vel.

Simhamukha looked at Muruga. He folded his hands and bowed to him, saying, 'I bow to you, valiant son of our supreme lord, Mahadeva and Parvati, who is the incarnate of the same Shakti I take for my mother, Kali. Accept my salutations before we commence our battle.'

Muruga returned the salutations as he said, 'Today, I proudly stand face to face with not only a worthy warrior but also a devotee of my mother whose devotion is unparalleled.'

The armies in the battlefield turned into an audience for this battle between two of the most powerful warriors to have ever existed. Simhamukha immediately pounced at Muruga as a lion pounces on a gazelle when going for the kill. Muruga, using his graceful speed, like a gazelle trying to avoid the death blow from a lion, darted out of the way and behind Simhamukha, again using the Vel to cut his head off. Again, the head grew back.

Muruga, without giving time to Simhamukha, jumped into the air and went for his head again. Simhamukha ducked out of the path of the Vel, came from below and threw Muruga away. Muruga, however, landed on his feet, throwing his Vel from mid-air. Simhamukha lost another head while being the only person in the multiverse to have touched Muruga in the battlefield. The two sparred, Muruga always managing to find innovative ways to cut Simhamukha's head off, and Simhamukha landing a dangerous blow every now and then, which Muruga took without even flinching.

The Veera brothers also arrived to see the fight. The day moved forward and not a single arrow was shot or a single life taken, while these two were fighting. They were inexhaustible.

This fight went on well past the afternoon. Simhamukha had been beheaded over nine hundred times, but he was still fighting fresh, managing to make Muruga back off multiple times, as well as avoiding his blows. For the nine hundred heads Simhamukha lost, Muruga had to attempt almost thrice the number of times with his Vel, which he merely used as a sharp tool.

Veerakendra whispered to Veeradheera, 'See how valiant our

Muruga is. He fights so gracefully and fiercely. He is indeed the god of war.'

Veerabahu, who overheard this conversation, turned to them and said, 'See how valiant Simhamukha is. The same Muruga disarmed Surapadma in a matter of seconds. The same Muruga, with his Vel, even stopped Bhadrakali's trident. When the same Muruga, who is none other than the son of Mahadeva and has the blessings of Shakti, who is ordained the god of war and victory by Mahadeva himself, is taking so long to finish and vanquish an enemy, imagine how great the enemy, Simhamukha, is. He knows that his end is imminent. Unlike Surapadma, he is not even entertaining the thought of running away or using Maya to trick us.'

The brothers agreed and admired Simhamukha's prowess.

Simhamukha was nearing his end. He fought with the same vigour, even though he was bloodied, but he was landing fewer blows than when he had started. Muruga moved faster with time, while his opponent was getting slower on account of his age and the constant beheadings. With Simhamukha's nine hundred and ninety-ninth head gone, only the last one remained, the original one, the lion head. Simhamukha was well aware of this, but that did not deter him one bit. He still went after Muruga with the same vigour as he had done at the very beginning.

Finally, Muruga kicked Simhamukha in the chest after avoiding his blow, felling the valiant fighter. He took to the skies in a leap, taking his full form, and hurtled down with his Vel. The skies darkened. The water blackened. The temperature dropped. The warriors started to shiver. They felt fear. Even the Veera brothers were not spared the feeling of inescapable fear that engulfed the battlefield. Muruga knew what was happening but he did not stop. Soldiers from both the armies went mad with fear and fainted.

The Vel had almost touched Simhamukha, who merely said, 'Kali,' welcoming his death.

Muruga and his Vel were propelled from the vicinity of

Simhamukha. Unlike the previous times, Muruga did not land on his feet.

Between Simhamukha and Muruga stood a monstrous figure, covering the entire distance between sky and earth. It was a woman, pitch black and unclothed. She had a girdle of freshly-cut arms around her waist, and her naked breasts were covered carelessly by a skull garland. Her twenty ears had mammoths for earrings. She had ten hands, each wielding a weapon, and ten legs wrapped by snakes instead of anklets. She carried a Ramdao, Trisula, sword, shield, Sudarshan Chakra, Vajrayudha, a freshly-severed demon head and a bowl of blood with a floating brain in it. The ninth hand had a bow with a spectral energy arrow and the tenth hand was over Simhamukha's head. She also had a closed third eye in each of her ten heads. Her tongue was hanging out, red in colour, as if it had just drunk fresh blood. Her hair, as black as her body, was long and flowed in all directions. She had been destroying a different universe and had come at the call of her son, Simhamukha.

The Veera brothers had fainted right before this form appeared, having survived the longest.

'Mother! You came for me, a mere mortal who has done nothing to deserve your grace!' said Simhamukha with tears in his eyes, seeing Kali for the first time, though he had unquestioningly worshipped her since time immemorial.

Muruga prostrated before the figure. Kali was, after all, a different and the most powerful aspect of his mother. He then stood up.

Kali saw him. Her eyes went to the Vel. She also noticed the third eye in each of his six heads. She recognized the potential of Mahadeva in the boy. She understood all. Her gaze turned to her fallen son, whose eyes were fixed upwards in a state of ecstatic Nirvikalpa Samadhi at the touch of his mother. She blessed Muruga as she nodded at him.

Muruga cast the Vel towards Simhamukha with Kali's hand

on his head. The Vel touched Simhamukha's neck and sliced it off his body. The head remained in Kali's hand; two pairs of legs with gigantic nails grew from it, followed by a body of a lion, golden in colour. As soon as Kali took her hand off its head, the lion grew in stature to match her in size.

The lion spoke, 'How fortunate am I, to have not only been slain by the son of Mahadeva and Mahashakti, but to also have been granted samadhi and also be resurrected by the divine mother herself, and be blessed to carry her on my back wherever she goes, for eternity.'

Then, it let out a roar that shook the multiverse. Kali sat on her lion and disappeared from the battlefield.

The fainted soldiers finally came to their senses, unaware of what had happened. They all saw that their valiant king, who had fought Muruga, was lying on the ground, a body without a head or life. They all wept, as did the Gana soldiers, who had come to admire the warrior Simhamukha was. Just as they were about to decide to end the battle for the day, one of the Asura soldiers attacked Muruga from behind with a gigantic scimitar.

Muruga sidestepped him, giving him a hard blow that sent him crashing to the ground. The Veera brothers were incensed at the audacity of an ordinary soldier and went after him, only to be stopped by Muruga.

'Get up, Surapadma,' said Muruga.

The Asura and Gana camps were shocked. The soldier stood up and transformed to Surapadma. He had disguised himself as an ordinary soldier using Maya and come to kill his opponent, unable to come to terms with the fact that his opponent was the god of war and son of Shiva.

'Aren't you ashamed of yourself? Your brother fought me valiantly, even though he knew that he would not be able to kill me. He died a thousand times, still continuing to fight me fairly, only as a true warrior could.

'This is not the Surapadma I came to slay. I came here to destroy the ruler of the multiverse, not a coward. I want you to leave the battlefield now, come to your senses and come as the warrior that you were. Come back as the Surapadma who fought and took over the multiverse. Come back as the Surapadma who walked through my army, including my brothers, as if they did not matter, on the second day of the war. I will fight you then. Go today and come tomorrow,' said Muruga.

Surapadma was drowning in shame. He had not only failed to kill his enemy, but was being chastised by him for attempting it in a shameful manner, in front of his own army. He could not face his soldiers. He disappeared from the battlefield and reappeared in his courtroom.

Amoghan came running as soon as he heard the noise of Surapadma wrecking his own courtroom. Amoghan rightly guessed that Simhamukha was dead but did not know what Surapadma had done.

'I am sorry, my emperor. Your brother was right. Your sons were right. I was right. We should have sought peace. Facing the son of Shiva was never a good option. We have lost everything now, but we still have you, my lord.

'It is not too late even now. Let us seek peace. Let us set the Devas free. After the millennia of torture we subjected them to, our vengeance is complete. Let us retain the rule of Veeramahendrapuri and Asurapuri, even if the multiverse is out of our grasp,' said Amoghan.

Surapadma took out his sword and beheaded his wise counsel and, with him, his wisdom.

Ajamukhi also arrived, to see her brother after hearing of Simhamukha's death. Her take was completely different though. She saw Amoghan's lifeless body in a corner and understood that the naysayer was gone.

She said to Surapadma, 'Brother, I told you! I told you that the Devas are up to no good. I told you that trusting Mahadeva would get us nowhere, for he is no different from Mahavishnu. He too will side with the Devas. We cannot trust anyone anymore. If only you had listened to my counsel earlier. If only you had taken me seriously. If only you had taken the cutting of my hand seriously and gone after Indrani and Indra. If only you had taken the killing of my sons seriously and gone after the wretched Agastya. If only you...'

She too faced the same fate as Amoghan, as she cribbed to Surapadma about being the victim in all these events. Surapadma then collapsed on this throne, falling asleep there itself, finally at complete peace.

In the Gana camp, they were celebrating the slaying of Simhamukha and were discussing how shameful Surapadma's vile act was, unbecoming of someone of his stature and standing. After all, he still was the ruler of the multiverse and one of the few beings capable of traversing the multiverse all by himself, something even Indra could not do by himself. It was a privilege and a gift that only the Trimurti and their spouses possessed, other than Muruga and Ganesha: Muruga by virtue of being born of Shiva's third eye and Ganesha having eaten the divine fruit.

Surapadma had done what no others could, establishing communication channels between the universes to facilitate governance. With two of the three Sura brothers gone, Surapadma was the only one left with that gift and ability. Muruga, in the meeting with his inner council, told them of what had happened and why they had been engulfed by the sudden feeling of fear.

He said, 'The only person who is left to come to the battlefield, leading the Asura army, is Surapadma himself. Tomorrow will be the last day of the war.

'Be warned that the battle tomorrow will be brutal, for Surapadma knows that he has no choice and he will come out with all guns blazing. Do not trust your eyes, for they will deceive you.

Do not let fear engulf you by the visions created by Surapadma. He is a thousand times more efficient in the use of Maya compared to Banugopan. Only Mahavishnu, Mahadeva, Mahamaya and I are better than him in wielding Maya. Do not believe your eyes and ears, for they will lie to you.

'I will take the lead in tomorrow's war, for Veerabahu has already faced Sura, as have the rest of the brothers, and you all know his might and prowess. Couple that with the insatiable feeling of vengeance and shame that is eating him and his grasp of Maya, and he will be practically be unstoppable. He will also not spare anyone like he did the last time, killing every single Gana he comes across.

'Veeramartanda, take the men you have left with you and leave for Asurapuri with Simhamukha's body. Give him due respect and conduct his funeral in the proper manner there, for Surapadma will not do it. Evacuate the kingdom. Agastya will come to you and guide you from there. I will come and visit you once the war is over tomorrow. Treat women and children with proper respect, but spare no Asura warrior left there. You can leave immediately. The rest of you can go and rest, for tomorrow will be a very long day.'

The Veera brothers did as they were told.

Kandashasti

The next day, Surapadma woke up calmly. His mind was clear. His face was serene. He went to his quarters, took a bath, came out and performed his regular worship of Mahadeva that had been on and off during the war.

Sura had communicated with his mother early that morning through his dream, which was one of the reasons behind his clarity.

'Mother! I have always looked up to you and followed your

order. Other than the Devas, whom you decreed as our sworn enemy, I have been good to the rest. I concede that I gave preferential treatment to Asuras, but who does not do it to their own clan? Why am I at this juncture? You are filled with utmost devotion for Mahadeva. Tell me, will I survive this war? Will the Asura race reign supreme at the end of this day?' he had asked.

Surasai had responded in his dream, 'My beloved son, you did well. You ruled the multiverse wisely. It is not what you did to the Devas that brought you to this juncture. The Devas lack devotion, whether to Mahavishnu or to Mahadeva. They were and are as selfish as ever.

'You are at this juncture because you allowed the Asuras to hurt and torture the rishis and devotees of Mahavishnu and Mahadeva. The karma accumulated by you, as their emperor, has led you to his point. It is with great pain that I tell you this: you will not survive this day. I shall transfer all the power of Maya that I have gathered through years of practice over to you. Remember your training and use it well.

'When one speaks of Muruga, they should speak of you. They should speak of how valiantly you fought and how much you pushed Muruga in the battle. They should speak of your abilities. Remember, even if you were to defeat Muruga or kill him today, you are a mortal and there will be a day in your life when you will die. Death is imminent for one and all. Life after death, through glory, is the highest honour one can earn. Earn this honour, my son. You have all my blessings.'

Surapadma then travelled to all of the universes through his thoughts, before waking up and making the final arrangements, for he now realized that this was his final day. He was calm and collected because he had done everything he could have and prepared himself for the worst possible outcome.

His wife, Padumakomalai, looked relieved. Her husband was back: she was happy to see him like that. She felt hope. He looked at her for a long time, but she did not budge, wondering what was going through his mind.

He spoke, 'My dear, I apologize for my behaviour over the last few days. My hunger for power and thirst for fame had given us so much. Unfortunately, the same also took everything from us. I have lost my brothers. We have lost our beloved children. There were so many opportunities when I could have stopped the events from unfolding in this manner, but I chose not to. You have been constantly crying from the day the messenger set foot in my court. Today, it will all be over. The war will be over, one way or another.'

Tears rolled down her cheeks, as she was unsure of what he meant. She had hoped that he would go for peace, but he still spoke of war.

'My emperor! Do not speak of war! Let us go and surrender to the son of Shiva. If he is as powerful as Shiva, he will also be as merciful. We do not need the kingdom. We do not need the multiverse. All we need is each other. Let us give up the mad rush for power. If apologizing to the enemy is shameful, let us go to the forest quietly and do penance for Mahadeva, seeking his grace to grant us Moksha. No one will be able to find us or look for us,' she said.

'No, my dear. Your words should induce wrath, but they does not. If I do not enter the battlefield today, I will have failed the sacrifices made by hundreds of thousands of Asuras for me. I will have failed Banugopan, Vajrabahu, Asurendran, Tarakasura, Krauncha, Agnimukha, Iranian and, above all, my beloved brother, Simhamukha. I must enter the battlefield. I must fight to the best of my ability. I owe it to them. I owe it to him.

'I am beyond shame and wrath now. Shame engulfed and drowned me when I committed the despicable act. It killed me when my enemy, a mere boy who I realize now was more than that, asked me to leave the battlefield and come back tomorrow. I was gripped by wrath when I beheaded Amoghan and Ajamukhi. Amoghan represented the best of wisdom that guided me and Ajamukhi represented the worst qualities I possessed. They are both gone now. I have only one thing left, duty. I will do my duty as an Asura and defend my kingdom with my life today.

'I want to thank you for being my wife and staying with me through the ups and downs. I want to thank you for making my pain yours, as you did with my joy. Above all, I want to thank you for believing in me, even when I did not, and for being patient with me when my behaviour went out of hand,' Surapadma concluded.

Padumakomalai fell to his feet and then rushed to hug Mahadeva's feet in the courtroom. Surapadma turned around, wore his full armour and left to address his army.

The army was assembled and even those who had not entered the war entered that day. Every single man in the Asura empire came that day. They did not want to live under the flag of anyone else but Surapadma. They knew that their emperor would go into the battlefield to finish the enemy or die trying. They wanted to be with him, no matter which of the two he accomplished.

Surapadma looked calmly at the assembled forces. It was full of anxious faces.

He spoke: 'My fellow citizens, we have been the most dominant force in all of the multiverse. We have ruled it undefeated until a week ago. No one would dare to look at us with the wrong intention. No one who is not an Asura would dare cross our path.

'What changed? What happened to us? Did we lose our courage? Our prowess? Our wrath? Our abilities? No. Nothing has changed. We are still as strong, as brave, as powerful and as vengeful as we ever were. When I built Veeramahendrapuri, I made sure that only the best of the Asura clan would be allowed to reside here. You are the best. You are the bravest of the Asuras. We will go out today. We will fight like only an Asura can. We will avenge the deaths of not only Banugopan, Iranian, Agnimukha and Simhamukha, but also the death of the innumerable Asuras caused by the invader.

'In today's battle, we will show the whole multiverse what an Asura is truly capable of when he is focussed. Only death will stop us today. Har har Mahadeva!'

The whole army chorused the same as they marched towards the battlefield where the Gana army was waiting for them, led by Muruga.

Muruga and Surapadma were face to face again, with the whole day ahead of them for battle. Muruga saw the clarity on Surapadma's face, as did the eight Veeras. They knew that they were going to be in for the battle of their lifetime. Muruga's chariot was helmed by Indra, who shuddered at the sight of Surapadma, whose eyes were fixed on Muruga's face. Vayu helmed Veerabahu's chariot, while Varuna helmed Veerakesari's. The other Kumaras rode chariots helmed by the other lords of the elements.

Surapadma could see Mahadeva in Muruga's face clearly, for his mind was no longer clouded. He knew that he was going to die and he vowed to fight a battle that would not only remove the stigma of last evening's events but would also change the structure of the multiverse as a whole. The battle, he vowed on Mahadeva's name, would be so fierce that one will not be able to take Muruga's name without taking his.

'Today is the last day of the battle, Muruga! Only one of us will be left alive when the sun sets!' thundered Surapadma.

Muruga smiled and said, 'Sura! You are among the greatest devotees of my father, Mahadeva. There is so much good in you. One can only imagine the depth of your devotion if it led my father to hand over the reins of the multiverse to you and give you so much power. You squandered it on vengeance. The only reason I did not finish you off on the second day was because I still believe that you have good left in you and can be redeemed. Surrender to me and I will spare your life.'

'There is no surrender in an Asura's life. There is only death in the battlefield for an Asura. If you want surrender, look at your charioteer. He is the one who is used to surrender, not out of humility, but out of pure selfishness. Even now, he is more concerned about himself than his son or his wife. He cries only for himself. My clan and I, on the other hand, sacrifice ourselves for the greater good of our race. We are true warriors, Muruga, and you will realize that today, as you did yesterday with my brother or the days before with my sons,' said Surapadma.

Both signalled their troops to advance and the armies rushed at each other. The Asura army was even more valiant and violent than it had been over the past five days. They were out to die and kill as many as possible before that. The Gana army felt the difference in their opponents. There was no fear. There was no holding back.

Surapadma, as he had done on the first day, launched the first offensive at the eight Kumaras. He was quicker, in fact, than the other day. But for the fact that their chariots were being driven by the elemental forces, they would have met the same fate as on the second day, or even worse.

Muruga did not shoot a single arrow. He was waiting for Surapadma to attack him. Muruga had ordered the Kumaras to aid the Ganas in fighting the reinvigorated Asura army, so they went after the Asuras. The first arrow that Sura shot at Muruga was an ordinary one, and even before Muruga could bat an eyelid, he followed it up with a flurry of Astras including the Agneyastra, Vayuastra, Varunastra and Vajrastra; all were aimed not at Muruga but at his army, who were slain in scores. While Muruga's attention was turned towards them, he was shot with the Pasupatastra. Muruga simply absorbed it, as it was his father's.

Indra wondered what Muruga was doing. Instead of slaying Surapadma, he was allowing him to take shots.

'Muruga! Why are you sparing him? Use your Vel!' said Indra.

Muruga looked down at Indra and said, 'His time is not up yet. He still has to exhaust all his Astras, granted to him thanks to the centuries of penance he did. He still has to exhaust all the merits earned by him from his good works, which will protect him. Do not fear, Indra, for when the sun sets, there will be no Surapadma.'

While Muruga was absorbing the Pasupatastra, Surapadma shot the Sammohanastra at Veerabahu and the Mohanastra at the rest of the regiment. They were all tied down, making them sitting ducks for the Asura army. Muruga took his Vel and shot it at the sky. Its light illuminated the whole area, setting his army free, as it had done with the Kumaras. Surapadma, meanwhile, shot all the other Astras, including the Narayanastra, at Muruga and the Vajrayudha at his chariot.

As the Vajrayudha was about to hit the chariot, Indra caught it and reclaimed it as his own. The Narayanastra and the others followed what the Pasupatastra had done. Surapadma was shocked. Not one of the Astras worked against Muruga. His own chariot shattered into pieces when eight arrows hit it from different directions. The Kumaras were surrounding him and shooting arrows at him. They anticipated him to fall to the ground again, but he soared into the sky. He was caught mid-air by Indra's Vimana, the very same Vimana that had deserted Indra at the mere stamp of his feet.

Surapadma showered arrows on the Gana army from the skies. Muruga blocked all the arrows with his own, bettering Sura's speed. Then, Indra took the form of a gigantic peacock which Muruga mounted and soared into the skies. They battled in the air, with Surapadma diverting Muruga every single microsecond by taking shots at his army or the Kumaras, all the while flying in the Vimana. Muruga flung the Vel at the Vimana, shattering it into million pieces, and Surapadma disappeared. He had switched to a different battlefield in a different universe.

Muruga, leaving Indra behind, followed suit. The battle raged on there. Muruga, using all his six hands with a multitude of weapons, singlehandedly fought against Surapadma and the army of Asuras assembled there. This army had its own general, warriors as powerful as Banugopan, and a whole lot of Asuras. Muruga did a quick job and turned his attention to Sura, who again did the same thing, switching to a different universe.

Unknown to the Ganas and Asuras, Sura had left the main battlefield in the hands of his two most trusted bodyguards, Singan and Anavan. They had also been discreetly trained in Maya and warfare by Surapadma himself. They were fighting inside the battlefield, masquerading as ordinary soldiers. Once Surapadma left, Singan, taking the form of Surapadma, soared to the skies and continued to rain arrows. The Ganas and the Kumaras who saw this were bewildered. Muruga was nowhere to be seen, while Surapadma was wreaking havoc. Anavan took claim as general, once he exposed who he was, taking the fight to Veerabahu.

Muruga was chasing Surapadma through multiple universes, squashing armies of Asuras in each and slaying them in their entirety. While the switching of universes may sound like a task that would take centuries, it all happened within seconds, for Surapadma and Muruga travelled at will and at the speed of thought.

This was the real Surapadma. This is how he, along with his brothers, ruled the universe. Simhamukha had not wanted to play tricks, instead relying on his might and strength. He saw Maya for what it was, being a devotee of Kali. Tarakasura was not afforded the opportunity to even think of any such plan. Further, he had lost the grace of Mahadeva once he stopped worshipping him. Surapadma, however, had both: devotion to Mahadeva and, through it, his grace, as well as the opportunity and intention to use all his abilities.

Seeing that there was no end to this and also realizing that his army and brothers were being massacred in his universe at that instant, Muruga did what he had done only once before: he took his Vishwaroopa. He, now, could see all the universes with all the activities happening in them. He raised one of his infinitely massive hands and from the palm, a shower of Vels flew, slaying the Asura armies in all of the universes, including the home one, erasing Asura warriors in all of them.

The Gana army cheered in the current universe.

Having seen the Vishwaroopa, unlike Indra and the Devas who required special eyes to be granted by Muruga, Surapadma was overwhelmed. His ego concentrated and collected in a dark corner of his mind. He could see himself in the Vishwaroopa as small as a mere speck of dust in the grand scheme of things. All his qualities disappeared at that moment and he became Nirguna. He bowed in reverence to Muruga as tears flowed from his eyes involuntarily and uncontrollably.

Then, Muruga disappeared, reappearing on the battlefield. The Ganas celebrated, while the entire Asura army was dead. They shouted, 'Vetri Vel, Veera Vel' at the top of their voices.

Surapadma also appeared in the current universe, standing in the middle of the massacred Asura army. He had summarily been defeated. He had nowhere to run or hide anymore. They fully expected Muruga to use his Vel now.

However, Surapadma sat down, closed his eyes, and started to chant a mantra. The Ganas, Kumaras and Indra were perplexed. No sooner had he finished, than all the dead Asuras sat up, except that each one of them was now a Surapadma.

The Ganas were terrified at the sight. The Kumaras did not know which one to go after. Hundreds of thousands of Surapadmas attacked the Ganas as they ran helter-skelter, while they were slain by the Surapadmas. The Kumaras fought against the multitudes of the enemy, only to realize that they only looked like Sura and did not have his power or ability. They remembered that Muruga had warned them not to believe their senses. They regained their composure and stepped up their attack on the Suras. Seeing them, the Ganas too did the same. However, Surapadma switched with the Suras fighting against the Kumaras, finishing them off one by one. Muruga, seeing what Sura was doing, threw his Vel, illuminating the whole place and removing the Maya, thereby exposing the Asura soldiers as mere zombies. The real Surapadma was going after Veerabahu and Muruga shot a powerful Astra at him. Surapadma again soared to the skies, taking the form of a gigantic phoenix spitting fire. The other seven Kumaras were dead. The Ganas finished off all the zombies, beheading them and rendering them useless.

The phoenix breathed fire from the sky, scorching the zombies and the Ganas as well. Muruga launched his Vel at Surapadma. As soon as the Vel touched it, the bird burst into smithereens, falling down as fine black sand which filled the battlefield and the ocean, and mixed with the air. It entered everyone who breathed, poisoning and killing them. Samudra too rushed out, seeing his subjects dying and his ocean filled up with sand. He sought refuge at Muruga's feet; Muruga threw his Vel. It went spinning, sucking up all the poison from the sand, rendering it harmless. Sura, not one to give up, grew into his full stature from each particle of sand, tearing apart and killing the Ganas who had breathed it in. Only a quarter of the Ganas and Devas were left, led by Veerabahu alone.

All the Suras combined to bring back the original Sura who exploded, becoming an indescribable formless black creature that sucked away the very air in the battlefield. More Ganas suffocated to death from lack of oxygen, and Muruga, seeing this, firmly planted his Vel in the earth and it illuminated everything around, purifying the air.

Seeing that he was being sucked into the Vel, Sura pulled back as much of the black mass as he could, before adopting his true form.

'I will not die before I have taken every single possible life with me, be it Gana, Kumara, Deva, Manushya or you,' said Surapadma, laughing defiantly at Muruga.

The Gana army looked around terrified, and saw what he said was true. He had killed eight Kumaras, and no Deva was left standing, except for Indra and Vayu; the Gana army was now merely one per cent of what had started the war on that day alone. Surapadma, by himself, had killed more Ganas than all the others combined.

Veerabahu, Indra and whoever was left on the battlefield were impressed beyond belief. How powerful was Surapadma? He was a single Asura in the battlefield, challenging the god of war and victory, and the son of Shiva, reinventing himself over and over again, and clearing out the army of Ganas. How powerful is Mahadeva truly if he, through a mere boon, can make someone so powerful? Above all, how powerful was Muruga, if he was destined to kill someone so powerful?

Muruga waved his Vel and it restored the Kumaras, the Gana army, and the Devas back to life and form, not as zombies but as they originally had been. Surapadma was taken aback. Before he could react, Muruga launched his Vel at Surapadma like a spear. The Vel went right through Surapadma: this was not the real Surapadma. He had switched himself with a shell as Banugopan had done. Seeing the Vel aimed at him, Surapadma had quickly disappeared. He was nowhere to be found. Everyone but Muruga was confounded.

Surapadma had hidden himself deep inside the ocean of Samudra as a tree. Muruga saw him for what he was and where he was and took his Vel. He worshipped his mother, Shakti and his father, Mahadeva. He launched the Vel at the tree, commanding it to slay the evil in Surapadma. He did not want to kill him, for he was still devoted to Mahadeva.

The Vel split the tree into two and it let out a cry that deafened the whole multiverse. For the first time in his entire existence,

Surapadma experienced immense pain, such that he could not bear without letting out a loud cry. He understood that Muruga was simply toying with him, for he could have very well done this on the first day of the war, or even before the war started. Muruga, for some reason, had been sparing him, but Surapadma did not want the mercy of his enemy anymore. He did not want the reason for his existence to be the mercy of his enemy and not the grace of his lord Mahadeva or his own might and prowess. He was, after all, not Indra.

One half of the tree took the form of a gigantic fighting rooster while the other half took that of a peacock. Another form fell between the two halves of the tree and both the birds as well as the form rushed aggressively at Muruga, to kill him.

Muruga merely raised his hand in the Abhaya Mudra and the rooster and the peacock bowed to him. The rooster climbed up the flag post of Muruga, becoming his emblem while the peacock became his Vahana. The form that fell between the two halves took the form of a gigantic snake and rushed towards Muruga. This was the valiant Asura's mammoth ego, separated from his form at each stage of the battle. This was the one holding Surapadma's virtues and vices together.

The peacock simply crushed the snake with its feet as it had the lord, the son of the supreme god and goddess, sitting on it, putting an end to the Asura and its clan. The snake died, crying out 'Mahadeva' one last time.

The war was finally over.

The Gana army shouted, 'Vetri Vel! Veera Vel!' as they celebrated the victory of their lord. The multiverse was now free from the tyranny of the Asura empire that had ruled it for a hundred and eight yugas.

Indra prostrated before this form of Muruga, as did the rest of the army, seeking his blessings. Muruga sat on a peacock before them, with his six heads, twelve arms, eighteen eyes and a Vel in his hand. His flag mast was by his side, with a rooster sitting on it and a snake was held down dead by his peacock Vahana.

Muruga blessed them all and said, 'You all will live a long, fulfilling, prosperous and blessed life, having fought the war without worry about your well-being, food or rest. Those who fast and worship me steadfastly and single-mindedly, chanting my name on these six days, will also get the same benefit as you all, who stood by me in this dreaded war.'

Shanta Parva

Aftermath

Muruga turned to the Kumaras and said, 'Go to Veeramahendrapuri. Evacuate everyone out of the city. Remember, the war is over. We have won. There are no more enemies to be vanquished. Whoever is left is now under my protection and my Vel's. Bring whoever comes of their own free will to the battlefield, which will temporarily serve as a camp.'

Muruga's attention then went to Indra, 'Indra, the war has been won. I am no longer your general. Here is my order for you: Go to Veeramahendrapuri along with the Kumaras. Take only that which was taken from you and Amaravati. The families of the Asuras are under my protection now, so cast off any thought you may possess of vengeance, unless you wish to incur my wrath. You are to take only your Kalpakavriksha, Airavata, Kamadhenu, the Devas and throne. Once you have collected them, fly them out to the battlefield. Then free your son and bring him here.

'Veeradheera, accompany Indra and aid him in his task. If he touches anything other than what belongs to him, be it object or people, do not hesitate to cut off his hands, as Sastha did with Ajamukhi.'

The jubilant Indra had entertained the idea of owning Veeramahendrapuri, its treasures, its women and everything else, being the man who won the war. His delusions, however, were shattered by Muruga's orders and he agreed to take only what belonged to him.

The Ganas went into the city of Veeramahendrapuri, the first time an enemy army set foot in the city since its inception. Just as Muruga had ordered, the Ganas gave due respect to every single Asura in the city, as they did to the Devas who were employed as slaves and servants. They treated everyone in the city with equal respect now that the war was over. They were quite in shock to find not even one male adult Asura left in the city. Every single one of them had come to the war, fought and perished. The city indeed lived up to its name.

Veerabahu was the one to scout the palace. He went in and saw Amoghan and Ajamukhi lying lifeless in a corner. His eyes darted to the beautiful statue of Mahadeva that looked like it had been recently worshipped. He was spellbound and prostrated before it. Then, he saw the figure of a woman at its feet.

He went to her and said, 'Mother! I am Veerabahu, brother of Muruga, who won the war against Surapadma by slaying him. The city of Veeramahendrapuri will sink in a matter of hours. I request you to humbly accompany me to the camp. I, on behalf of my brother, assure you that you will be treated with respect and no harm will come to you. If you do not trust the intentions of others, I will take you as my mother and you can stay with me, for you are a devotee of Mahadeva, who my father is.'

The figure did not budge.

'Mother,' he called out gently for a second time. He touched the soles of her feet, as if he were seeking her blessings, trying to wake her up.

Her lifeless body fell off from Mahadeva's feet. It was Padumakomalai: she had left her body the moment her husband had left for war. Surapadma as well as Padumakomalai were certain that he would not return.

The whole city marched towards the battlefield. Catching the sight of the battlefield, their faces lit up instead of crumpling. Between Sura's resurrection of them as zombies, being showered with arrows by Muruga and then being scorched by the Vel, they were unidentifiable. They were filled with pride. This confounded the Devas and even the Kumaras.

One of the Devas asked an Asura woman, whose husband was a kind master, if she did not feel even a single pang of pain at the sight of the massacre. She replied that it was not in an Asura's blood to cry for the brave who perished in battle. The emotion that was evoked in them at such a sight was pride. She started to sing the praise of the fallen warriors and the rest of the Asura women joined her. Not a single tear was shed in the battlefield. The Asura women celebrated the bravery and courage of their fallen kith and kin. Even the Devas could not help but begrudgingly admire their enemy.

Once they all arrived, Muruga addressed them, 'Dear people of Veeramahendrapuri, I am Muruga, son of Shiva, the one who defeated your valiant emperor. Be assured that your emperors are the most valiant and powerful opponents anyone could have ever met in a battlefield. Your emperor was not slain by me. He is always with me in the form of the rooster sitting on top of my flag mast and in the form of the peacock which will be heralded as my Vahana. The rooster, which is higher than me, symbolizes my respect for his fearlessness and him becoming my Vahana was possible because of his unflinching devotion to my father.'

The Asura folk bowed down Muruga, not only for the respect that he had rendered to their emperor or for his superior prowess in the battlefield that he was able to destroy all three of the brothers, but also for his divine grace and form that he had inherited from his father. The Asura clan, which steadfastly worshipped Mahadeva, accorded the same devotion to Muruga, if not more, for he had come in person and given them his full grace and blessings.

'Ask for any boon you seek,' said Muruga as they all prostrated before him.

'Be with us, forever. Stay with us. We will be safe under you as we were under Sura. That is all we seek,' they said.

'I will make this place my residence, be here and protect you all forever from any and all harm. Those who have surrendered to me unconditionally will be protected by my Vel and my peacock,' said Muruga.

He then directed them to leave for the mainland. While all

this was happening, Indra went and got Jayanta and the imprisoned Devas back. Muruga had intentionally sent Indra to recover them, so that they would get an opportunity to reconcile. They did reconcile, as Indra explained briefly to them all the effort that he had put in, right from getting Kamadeva to make a match, getting Mahadeva married to Parvati, to being Muruga's charioteer as well as his Vahana during the battle. Jayanta forgave his father but regretfully could never forget Indra abandoning everyone or trust him ever again. He was more eager to meet Muruga, who had indeed managed to defeat not just one but all three of the brothers.

They also came to the battlefield. Jayanta rushed to Muruga's feet, as did the other Devas who had been held captive and tortured. As soon as they rose, all the physical deformities caused by the Asuras vanished and those in the process of healing were instantly healed. Muruga blessed them. He also praised Jayanta for keeping up the morale and fighting courageously for his clan. Muruga, who can see all, had seen his battle with Surapadma as well and came to respect him as a warrior.

Jayanta asked, 'Is my mother alright, my lord?'

Muruga replied, 'She is in Kailash,' which more than assuaged all his concerns.

Muruga then directed his generals, the Devas, the Asura folk and everyone to leave the battlefield for Skandamadana, where they were treated with hospitality and equality. By Muruga's grace, the Devas as well as the common Asura folk felt remorse for their actions and sympathized with their erstwhile enemies' situation: Devas were remorseful of the past and Asuras of the present. They both looked towards a bright future based on non-interference, if not cooperation.

Sunk

*V*eeramartanda arrived the next morning at sunrise. He also brought the Asura folk from Asurapuri, who were as brave as the citizens of Veeramahendrapuri. However, unlike the folks in Veeramahendrapuri, the Devas and the Asuras in Asurapuri were friendlier with each other. The Devas from Asurapuri both helped and consoled the kith and kin of the fallen Asuras. They had nothing but the kindest of words for their fallen emperor, Simhamukha.

Muruga then summoned Samudra the next day. Samudra appeared instantly, prostrating before Muruga and vowing to serve him unconditionally. He also praised Surapadma's graceful gesture of allowing Samudra to be a neutral party in the war.

Muruga said to Samudra, 'Samudra! I want you to build up the landmass, allowing people in Skandamadana to reach the mainland in Chendur. Escort them safely to the mainland and arrange for their food. I am going to sink both Asurapuri and Veeramahendrapuri along with Skandamadana and all islands created artificially for the Asuras.'

Samudra said, 'I will do as you command, my lord. May I make a request?

Muruga replied, 'Yes, go ahead.'

'Can you leave a spot of land? Something that stands as a reminder of the war that was fought here and carries the imprint of your footstep, thereby making it holy?' asked Samudra.

'So be it! I will leave a small hill on Skandamadana, which will be the last of the land masses in the islands that were artificially built,' blessed Muruga.

Samudra did as he was ordered. Led by the Veera brothers, the folk left for Chendur and were housed in an elaborate city that was built for them by Vishwakarma, according to the orders of Muruga.

Eventually, Muruga took a gigantic form, stood on the hill holding the Vel, worshipped his parents and ordered the Vel to sink all the artificial islands that were ruled by the Asura clan, along with the battlefield where the battle was fought, only leaving the spot under Muruga's feet.

The Vel whizzed past, destroyed both the islands, whatever was left of the circles, and the battlefield along with the slain warriors' corpses, thereby fulfilling Durvasa's curse as well as Muruga's father's command. Finally, it came back to Muruga, who then took off on his peacock and landed in Chendur.

Celebrations

*I*ndrani, along with Devayani, rushed to Chendur upon hearing the news that the war was over and her son was safe. Devayani and Jayanta were introduced to each other. Indrani came along with Nandi, who considered it his prime task to protect any and every devotee of Mahadeva, and Ganesha, who was eager to see his brother.

Upon seeing Ganesha, Muruga, who was in the warrior mode, switched to a kinder aspect, rushing to hug his brother. They shared a long hug. Both cherished each other and told each other how much they had missed one another. Ganesha then went on to hug his other brothers, the Veeras. Agastya too had come to Chendur with Veeramartanda.

Mahadeva and Parvati appeared too, as did Mahavishnu and Brahma along with their spouses, to congratulate Muruga on the great victory. There were elaborate celebrations with songs sung in praise of Muruga, not only praising him for his beauty but also for his grace, prowess, kindness and the power with which he set the multiverse free.

The celebrations went on in Chendur for days. The Veera brothers, guided by Agastya, were engaged in relocating the Asura clan in and around Chendur, allowing them to mix and live with the Manushyas, rishis and others living in the region. They were all united by their devotion to Mahadeva and Muruga, with the common language of Tamizh between them. With this, Agastya completed the task for which he had been sent southward to balance the universe.

By the end of the celebrations at the end of the Kritika month, Vishwakarma had rebuilt Amaravati to resemble Veeramahendrapuri, as requested by Jayanta, much to the chagrin of Indra. The Devas decided to take leave and came to seek Muruga's blessings. Indra was the first to bid farewell. Next was Jayanta, who came and said, 'My lord! You destroyed the Asura clan. You rescued the Devas and freed them from their fall. With the whole multiverse being yours, is there anything that we can give you as a token of our gratitude?'

That was when Indra was reminded of his promise to grant Devayani in marriage to Muruga. Before he could speak, Indrani spoke: 'Do not worry, Jayanta. We have our beloved Devayani, your sister whom you met once, when we came to Chendur, to give to Muruga. She is a treasure beyond treasures, and Muruga is the only one worthy of marrying her.'

Narada nudged Indra to keep his word, as did Brahma.

'I, Indra, king of Devas, in this gathering of all divinity, propose to give the hand of Devayani to Muruga, who, as my general, fought and conquered the vile Asuras, thereby earning the right to marry her,' said Indra.

Narada and Brahma almost snickered at Indra's conceit, but they all chose to ignore it finally.

Mahadeva, who was also present there, asked Agastya to choose an ideal place and date for the wedding. Agastya said that Parankundram would be the ideal place, for it had hills, which were forever tied to the folklore of Muruga and had the ability to hold the weight of all the people who would attend the wedding. The ideal date, he said, would be Phalguni month, Uthira star, the same date when Mahadeva had married Parvati, making it one of the most suitable dates for matrimony.

Ganesha said that he would officiate the wedding. As with the wedding of Mahadeva and Parvati, it had the complete attendance of the who's who in the universe. Muruga, who always looked magnificently graceful, looked even more handsome in the garb of a bridegroom. The whole universe celebrated the wedding.

The wedding happened as per the rituals prescribed in the scriptures, with complete acceptance not only from the bride's and groom's sides but from the entire universe, without any naysayers. With the wedding, Muruga, through the virtue of being the son-in-law of Indra, solidified his relationship with the Devas who were now pegged to take back the control of the universe.

Once the marriage ceremony was over, Indra took the bride and the groom, whom he no longer felt indebted to for he was his son-in-law, to Amaravati, where they resided for a few days before they went off to Kailash. Days went by. Indra again began to feel restless. He was still to be crowned as the emperor of the universe. He was hoping to regain control of the entire multiverse which had been ruled by the Asura brothers. He wanted everything because, in his mind, he believed that he was the winner of the war. He did not know who to ask and, as he always did, he ran to Brahma.

Brahma told him that he had not received a command from Mahadeva and without his word, there was nothing he could do about it. He offered to come with him to Mahadeva, if he so desired. Indra asked him to accompany him, inviting Narada, who was there to join them.

The three of them went to Mahadeva. Mahavishnu and Parvati were there as well in a meeting, with Muruga and Ganesha listening in keenly.

Clampdown

*W*hen Brahma, Indra and Narada arrived, Nandi, who had already been informed to allow them, welcomed them inside.

'I was about to ask for your presence, Brahma. It is indeed good timing that you came in by yourself. As far as you Indra, you can also be present, for this also concerns you. Narada will be here as witness, as will Nandi,' said Mahadeva.

Indra felt elated. He was going to be crowned the emperor of the multiverse and not merely the universe which he was ruling. He was going to be as powerful as Sura himself. He was going to become the highest among the gods. The whole multiverse was going to come under his feet. No Asura would dare to look up at him anymore with Muruga as his son-in-law and him as the emperor of the multiverse.

'I had a discussion with Mahavishnu, my esteemed and wise friend, without whose knowledge I could do nothing, based on a suggestion from Parvati. I had tasked Ganesha to work out the details. Mahavishnu too is aware of this and added his inputs and gave his concurrence.

'I, as the guardian and destroyer of the multiverse, based on a suggestion by Parvati who is Adi Shakti incarnate herself, after receiving concurrence from Mahavishnu, have decided that there will no longer be a ruler of the multiverse. Each universe will operate independently. Except for myself, Parvati, Mahavishnu, Mahalakshmi, Brahma, Saraswati, Ganesha and Muruga, no one else will be able to access the multiverse anymore. Like immortality, such a boon will not be granted to anyone. This is for the benefit and well-being of all lives in the multiverse.

'Further, as suggested by Mahavishnu, the current universe will be divided into different astral planes to house different races. The earth shall belong to Manushyas, rishis and Asuras, while the

Devas will inherit a separate plane with Amaravati as its capital, having no direct control over earth except for the elements and the Navagraha. Yama, to ensure that his duty is not disturbed by anyone anymore, will get a separate plane and will report only to me, for his task of destruction is a fragmentation of mine. No one will be able to travel across planes except if required by their duty. Grant to travel across planes at will can be given as a boon, but only after severe penance. Obviously, those who have access to go anywhere in the multiverse will have access to all planes. This planar division will happen in all universes.

'As most of you know, there is only one Kailash and it will continue to remain the focal point, accessible from any universe and plane. Mahavishnu's Milky Ocean and Vaikunta will constitute a separate plane, independent of all others, which can be accessed only by his grace and blessings. Guided by Mahavishnu, Ganesha has planned it and, with Muruga, will execute the above activity,' concluded Mahadeva.

Indra was crestfallen. He was no longer even the ruler of the universe. He was delegated to merely being content with ruling over the Devas alone, based out of Amaravati.

Brahma said, 'I wholeheartedly welcome the idea, Mahadeva. I would also like to have Satyaloka as a separate plane, just like Vaikunta. Neither do I need to nor have I accessed the multiverse. I do not even recollect how to access them. I would like to be in Satyaloka and perform my duty of guiding the creations, if required, as their progenitor.'

'I concede to your request, Brahma. As one of the Trimurti, you do have the right to access the multiverse. If you require us to tell you how, you can ask us anytime,' said Mahadeva to Brahma.

Indra was even more disappointed. He could no longer run to Satyaloka or Vaikunta at will to seek help whenever he ran into trouble. Mahadeva turned to Mahavishnu, who nodded in agreement. All three of them were in concurrence.

Mahadeva then turned to Brahma and said, 'Grandsire of progeny, please be kind enough to crown Indra as the king of the Devas in Amaravati. We all will visit the event.'

He then turned his attention to Narada, Muruga and Ganesha and said, 'Children, go ahead and complete the task in a week. Narada, spread the word to all those who would be affected by this move. In a week's time, this will come into effect. Inform the rishis, Danavas, Nagas, Gandharvas and anyone who you think should be informed.'

He then turned his attention to all and said, 'As always, all of you can come to Kailash anytime you please. With respect to Kailash, nothing has changed.'

Mahavishnu decreed that no one would be able to reach Vaikunta unless they have complete and absolute devotion towards him or Mahalakshmi. Brahma also said that Satyaloka's doors were shut for anyone who was not a rishi or belonged to the first generation of his offspring. The only exception was those who come to see him on the quest of knowledge which he alone can share. Indra left for Amaravati. Brahma, on an auspicious day, crowned him the king of Devas and left for Satyaloka.

Dawn

At the end of week, Muruga and Ganesha efficiently cut off all of the universes as ordered by Mahadeva and planned by Ganesha. Muruga then said, 'Father, with your permission, I would like to crown the Nava Kumaras kings of their own kingdoms in the land that was liberated from the Asura brothers. Along with them, I also seek your approval to crown Jwala as the queen of her own kingdom.'

'Do you not seek to rule the erstwhile Asura empire on earth, Muruga?' asked Mahadeva.

'No, Father. I would like to spend my time doing penance towards you and helping those who have surrendered to me as and when they need me. That was the third thing I wanted to request you. I request you to grant me permission to make the erstwhile Asura empire to the south of the Vindhyas my abode. I gave a boon to the fallen Asura clan that I would be there and protect them always,' said Muruga.

'I am pleased with your requests, my son. None of them came from selfishness and you do not gain anything from them. You have my blessings,' said Mahadeva.

'Brother, please come and crown them as the officiator,' said Muruga to Ganesha.

Muruga and Ganesha then went south. Muruga summoned Jwala and the Nava Kumaras to Thiruparankundram. He, along with Devayani, informed the Nava Kumaras of his desire. Jwala too accepted any decision coming from Muruga as if it were coming from Mahadeva himself. However, Jwala and Veerabahu together said, 'We will obey your command, Muruga. We however have a request on our side. We request you to be our emperor. We want to be under your umbrella.'

Muruga responded, 'No, my brothers and sister.' Jwala was in highest heaven when Muruga addressed her as his sister. He went on, 'You all have earned the right to rule. You are more than capable of ruling the land with benevolence and maternal love towards your subjects. You are powerful enough to quash any enemy who might come here with the wrong intentions. Rule wisely.'

The Nava Kumaras and Jwala bowed to him. It was Veerabahu who was a bit hesitant. Muruga understood something was eating him inside. 'Ask, my dear Veerabahu,' said Muruga.

'My brother! The thought of being away from you hurts us. The thought of being away from Kailash pains us furthermore,' said Veerabahu.

'That is not the only thing on your mind, my beloved brother.

Ask the other question too,' said Muruga.

'Why did you not kill off Surapadma on the final day as soon as the battle started?' asked Veerabahu.

'As you all know, Surapadma was still as devoted to Mahadeva as ever. That is the prime reason. However, the other reason is that he still had hordes of divine Astras that had to be redeemed and returned to their rightful owners. So, I took the brunt of all his divine Astras by ending their existence outside their creators.

'Further, Surapadma still had command over other universes. With the plan to divide them into individual entities already in the thoughts of my father, and my brother working on it, I felt that it was essential to end all Asura affiliation towards him across the multiverse. This was the reason I allowed him to travel across the multiverse for battle.

'Also, I had to separate his devotion, prowess and ego, so that I could kill his ego, which was the root cause of all the problems the multiverse faced. A darshan of Vishwaroopa was essential for that. The travel across multiverse facilitated the need to show the Vishwaroopa. That was when the snake that the peacock crushed came into a being as a separate existence within Surapadma.

'I also wanted to drain him of the power that propelled his ego. So, I let him become the black formless creature as well as the poison sand, which exhausted him. After all the above were accomplished, I cast the Vel to simply isolate the evil inside him, which became a snake, giving form to his ego.

'Finally, his own wisdom and power in the form of a peacock, and his devotion in the form of a rooster came out on their own. His wisdom backed by his prowess crushed his ego backed by his evil, setting him free. Does that answer your second question, Veerabahu?' asked Muruga.

'Yes, my lord,' said Veerabahu as the Nava Kumaras listened intently.

'As far as missing Kailash goes, I have cast a broken piece

of it and planted it here to the south of the Vindhyas. It was the mound on which I elaborated on the true meaning of Aum to my father. You can go there, and you will feel no difference between being there and being in Kailash. Call it Swamimalai after the name given to me by my father, Swaminatha,' said Muruga.

'About missing me, my dear brothers, I am always with you and will always be. I have only one piece of advice for you. Never forget the circumstances under which you came to power, lest history should repeat itself, for as per the boon given to the Asuras, I will come to their rescue were they under any threat for no fault of theirs. If you ever need anything from me, think of me and I will be there for you,' Muruga said.

'The place where we based our operations, call it Thiruchendur as a mark of respect for Father, who visited the place. Of course, you have Thiruparankundram, where my marriage happened, if you were to miss Mother and Brother. Above all, you all have Thiruvannamalai. The place is Father himself, as it is as holy as Kailash, where Father resides,' said Muruga.

'Enough blood has been shed and enough lives have been lost. That should be enough for a hundred centuries. Let the next millennium be that of peace under the able leadership of the ten of you. You always have my backing, support and blessings,' concluded Muruga.

Upon hearing the words of Muruga, all ten of them were very happy and elated to know that they would never be cut off from Mahadeva or their own lord, Muruga.

As Muruga requested, they divided their territories and Ganesha crowned them on an auspicious day and time. It was a time of peace and equality for people of all races. Wars were long forgotten. There was no taxation or requirement for one. Agriculture and weaving were the prominent occupations, as was fishing in the seabound territories. Trade flourished and the ten kingdoms to the south of the Vindhyas flourished in peace and harmony.

Ganesha left for Kailash after bidding farewell, for now, to his brother.

Prema Parva

Premier Partie

Nambiraja

*N*ambiraja was a small king, ruling the forest atop a hill named Thanigaimalai. His subjects were predominantly a hunting tribe. Much like Himavat and Daksha, he wanted a daughter. He had worshipped Muruga diligently as prescribed by Agastya and Avvai. Valli, as he named her, was found in the forest, entangled among sweet creepers, from which came her name. He immediately took it that she was the child he had been praying for and took her home. He, along with his wife and tribesmen, brought up Valli with care and devotion.

The tribe was completely devoted to Muruga. They considered themselves slaves of Muruga and accepted him as their lord. Being brought up in a devout family in a pious environment, Valli came to worship Muruga and wanted to be his for her entire life. Her devotion turned to love and she started seeing him as the one she was destined to marry, without being aware that it was indeed her destiny to be married to Muruga.

If her devotion to Muruga was one of her defining attributes, the other was her fearless character. There was no danger that she would back down from. Tigers, cheetahs, bears and what not, none of them scared her in the slightest. She outdid the men of her tribe when it came to her hunting prowess.

Nambiraja gifted the best of his men to Veeramartanda to fight the war when he learned that Muruga was going to take on the mighty Asura ruler. Valli desperately wanted to join the war but her father flatly refused, saying that Muruga had entrusted her to him to be kept safe and handed over to him when he came for her. She was not to leave the edges of the forest under any circumstances. After swearing on the name of her lord to not leave the forest, she could not leave for the war. The men who went with Veeramartanda, stayed with him to help him at different stages with different tasks.

With the best men away, the job of being the chief among hunters fell to her. She was tasked to protect the fields that were the hunting grounds for not only birds, rats or other small animals, but also wild elephants. If there was one thing that terrified her, it was wild elephants. Even the calf of an elephant was enough to send her running for the trees. She saw this opportunity to lead their pack and took on the task of protecting the fields herself. She wanted to prove to herself and the rest of her tribe that she was fully capable of facing and overcoming her fear of elephants but always backed out at the last minute.

Destiny, however, had different plans for her for that day.

Valli

*V*alli got up according to her usual routine. She took a bath at the waterfalls and then went to her Muruga temple and worshipped him to her heart's content, telling him of her yearning for his love and affection. Valli was planning to send Kumba, a hunter who had slain elephants before, to protect the fields that day.

'Narayana! Narayana!' said the sage who crossed her path at the temple.

Valli bowed to him paying her respects and said, 'Who are you, respected seer? What do you seek? If you are seeking alms, kindly come in and accept our hospitality. If you are looking for war with the strange weapon you wield, then I am more than prepared to face you as the chief of hunters in this kingdom.'

'I am Narada, my child. The weapon you speak of is a Tambura. It is a musical instrument used as accompaniment for singing. I wander around the worlds and came over here during my rounds,' said Narada with a gentle and friendly smile.

'I apologize for my rudeness and ignorance, respected sage. Can I request you to accept our hospitality as a sign of your forgiveness?' asked Valli.

'Yes, my child. I will accept your hospitality, provided that I am offered the same in the manner of accompanying you where you are going now,' said Narada.

'As you wish, seer,' said Valli and Narada accompanied her to Kumba's hut.

'Where are you going, my child, if I may ask?' asked Narada.

'I am going to the hut of one of my clansmen to order him to go to guard our millet farms,' said Valli.

'That is strange. Orders are usually given to those who come and take it. It is rare to see someone going to give an order to a subordinate,' said Narada.

'There is no subordinate or superior in our kingdom, seer. All are equal citizens. My father merely carries the responsibility of running the administration. I simply carry the responsibility of being the chief among the tribesmen for protecting our kingdom,' said Valli proudly.

'Quite interesting,' said Narada. 'Why is the chief going to give an order to a soldier to guard something as simple as a millet farm personally? Does she see the task as beneath her?'

'No, seer. I do not want to lie to you. I am terrified of elephants. There was an attack of elephants yesterday and, therefore, I am asking Kumba to go instead of me,' said Valli.

'That is a shame. Can I ask which god you worship who has failed to give you the required courage?' asked Narada.

This instantly made Valli angry.

'I am letting your snide remark towards my god and lord Muruga pass only because you are a guest. Otherwise, I would cut your head off for insulting my lord,' said Valli.

'My point still stands. Muruga, the god of war and victory, has failed to give you the courage. Is it his fault or yours?'

asked Narada.

'It is my fault. If, because of my fault, Muruga were to get a bad name, then it should be me who goes on protection duty today, even if it means my death,' said Valli. She immediately turned around and went towards the mud path leading to their millet farm on the top of the hill in the middle of the forest without informing her father.

Hunter

She went to the millet farm and climbed atop the observation tower meant to give a good view while protecting the watcher as well. She carried a shepherd's sling and a spear with her, along with a bow and arrow. She was adept at throwing the spear as well as using it as a fighting weapon. Her aim was perfect. She preferred to hunt with her spear more than her bow and arrow, as it gave her more control against fast moving animals that were coming for her.

She heard some rustling in the forest adjacent to the farm. Her hand rushed to her spear. She did not want to think that it was an elephant. Being an experienced hunter good enough to lead her tribesmen, she waited to pass judgement, for it could as well be a deer.

It was a deer. It darted across the forest's edge and saw the tower. It twitched its ears and looked back and forth. It then darted through the field, running away in the other direction towards the forest. It was clear to her that the deer was running away from something. She was not sure what it was but was relieved to think that if it was a mad elephant, the deer would not have waited. It was probably a cheetah or a tiger, something she had hunted before and was not afraid of.

She loosened her grip on the spear, took a stone, loaded it into her slingshot and threw it in the direction that the deer came from.

'Aaahh!' she heard a cry.

Satisfied that it was not an animal, for it sounded human, she suddenly realized that she had accidentally hit someone, probably a hunter, for the deer would not run away scared from a seer.

She got off the tower and rushed through the field to take a look. As she was halfway through the field, a masculine figure walked out of the woods. He was a hunter, clad in tigerskin wrapped across one of his shoulders, leaving the other free. His broad shoulders and massive chest; clear face with a moustache, broad forehead and long hair held off his face by a bandana made out of snakeskin; bearskins shoes and dark brown eyes made him an attractive hunter. He had a spear hung on his back, ready to be pulled off and used. He had his bow in his arm and a quiver full of arrows.

She noticed a small wound on his forehead, from which he was bleeding. She realized that she had struck him and rushed to him.

Once near him, she said, 'I apologize, sir. I thought it was a tiger or a cheetah, based on how the deer you were chasing darted across the field. Let me apply some herbs to it and it will be alright.'

'The only good thing about your hunting skill is your aim,' said the hunter arrogantly. 'Will a deer dart so slowly in a straight line if it had seen a tiger or a cheetah chasing it? I had the deer in my view with my arrow ready to shoot. But for you I would have got my deer.'

'Speak carefully to me sir, for I am the daughter of Nambiraja. The only reason I am forgiving you your condescending speech is because I injured you and, if what you say is true, I cost you your game,' said Valli with a hint of authority.

'Or else what? The only reason you are still standing here after hurting me is because of your beauty. I am only forgiving you for it is someone as beautiful as a deer who has cost me another,' said the hunter in a flirtatious tone.

'You, sir, do not realize the gravity of what you are doing. I can not only defeat you in any of the activities you think you are good at, but also kill you all by myself if I chose to,' said Valli.

'And that is precisely what makes you even more beautiful and attractive. You are the perfect huntress for his hunter,' was the hunter's response.

Valli became irate at this unwarranted attention she was receiving. She quickly put her hand into her sling bag, took out a stone and loaded it into the slingshot.

'One more word and I will give you one more wound to match the one you have on this side of your forehead. Another word and the next one would go for your throat, killing you,' said Valli, not realizing that the man in front of her was none other than Lord Muruga.

'Oh! I am scared!' he said mockingly with a radiant smile.

'You should be,' she responded.

'See that bird,' she pointed to a bird perched on a far-off tree, which had a single broken feather standing out, still sticking to its body. She launched her stone at the bird, and it hit the feather, removing the feather that had been bothering the bird.

'That feather could have been your Adam's apple,' she said.

Muruga came to understand and appreciate her prowess, which was an additional characteristic that made him fall in love with her even more.

'You just proved that you are the perfect huntress for this hunter. I am handsome, young, strong and an accomplished hunter, as you can see from the tigerskin and bearskin. You are young, beautiful and have the perfect aim and control, as you just exhibited. We would make the perfect couple. Marry me,' said the hunter.

'One can skin dead tigers and bears. The only hunting expertise you have exhibited is missing a deer,' said Valli in a demeaning tone.

The hunter pointed to the feather that Valli had removed, which was floating in air. He took his spear and aimed it at the feather. He released his spear and it took the feather and nailed it to the tree. Valli could not help but be impressed. She had hit an almost stationary target while he hit a target that was moving beyond his control.

'I apologize for my remark about your skills. However, I have vowed that I would only wed my lord Muruga and no one else,' said Valli apologetically.

'Is this Muruga the same one who went to war with Surapadma?' asked the hunter innocently.

'Yes,' she replied.

'I heard that he is already married to the daughter of Indra and got a huge bounty of riches as a gift. Do you honestly believe that he would come here and would want to marry a huntress from a tribe living on a mountain? The richest thing you can offer him is elephant tusks and to collect enough tusks, you would have to wait for all the elephants to die for an entire millennium to even get his attention,' said the hunter.

At the mere mention of elephants, she let out a shudder. She realized that she was in front of him and hoped that he had not noticed the shudder.

'Sir, you do not know Muruga. He is the kindest of the gods. He is our clan's deity as well. What I am offering him is a lot more than all the riches in the universe. I am offering him my complete devotion and pure love which is his alone, whether he chooses to accept it or not. Devayani was given as a gift to him, along with his riches for winning the war.

'She does not love him as much as I do. All she can give him is the devotion of a wife to her husband. I can give him the love that he would never get from anyone else,' said Valli.

The hunter, Muruga, was impressed at her steadfastness.

'You will end up getting old at such a young age, like Avvai, waiting for him. Marry me. We will make the happiest couple in the whole of the forest, which is my kingdom. We will live in the mountain forests that I have so come to love and have never left as its guardian,' implored the hunter.

'You seem to know an awful lot for someone who claims to be the king of the forest and have never left it. If you truly have never left the forest, how is it possible, sir, for you to know about Avvai or Sura?' asked Valli.

'I am...' the hunter started when he heard footsteps.

Narada, as instructed by Muruga, had gone to inform Nambiraja of Valli going all by herself. He had come along to the farm on the pretext of giving her food, to make sure that she was alright. Upon hearing footsteps, the hunter disappeared. She, having turned her head to see who was coming, turned back to see him gone. There was a new tree at the edge of the field, which she noticed.

Old Man

*N*ambiraja rushed to the spot, only to find her all by herself in the middle of the field. 'What is wrong, my child? What are you doing off the tower in the middle of the field? I thought you were going to ask Kumba to come for duty,' said the king.

Valli replied, 'Father, I thought I heard a noise and came to check. It was a deer that darted out of the field and rushed out through the other end. I threw a stone using the sling towards whatever the deer was running from and heard a growl. I came to make sure that it does not enter the field.'

She did not want to make the hunter a victim of her tribesmen's wrath now that he had disappeared. She did not want his blood on her conscience.

'Take care, my child. Do you want me to stand guard with you? I heard an elephant trumpet loudly. You can leave if you want,' said Nambiraja.

'No, Father. It is my duty. I will be here and face whatever I have to in order to protect our millet farm,' said Valli.

'As you wish, my child,' said Nambiraja. He never made her do anything she did not want to do or stopped her from doing what she wanted.

'Can I have some food?' asked a voice from behind them.

They turned around and saw a very old man in ochre robes. Valli noticed that the tree was gone.

'Yes, sir. Can I know who you are?' asked Nambiraja.

'I am a Muruga devotee. I roam around in the forest and worship him in his abodes. I was roaming around different forests and ended up coming here,' said the old man. His face was heavily wrinkled and his back was bent from age. He used a stick to walk.

'Please accept our hospitality. This is my daughter, Princess Valli, of our tribe. We consider ourselves slaves of Muruga. By extension, we are slaves of any of his devotees. Valli will take care of you,' said Nambiraja.

'Thank you, kind king. Thank you, princess,' said the old man.

Nambiraja left, satisfied that his daughter was not alone and all by herself. Even if her companion was an old man, he was someone who roamed around the forest and if he did so at his age, he was sure to have good instincts or god's grace that protected him. Irrespective of what protected him, it would protect his daughter as well.

Valli took the old man by his hand to the tower and gave him the millets and honey she was crunching. The old man thanked her as he ate.

As soon as he took the first mouthful, he said, 'I shouldn't have taken it. My teeth are no good. If I were to swallow it, I would need water.'

Valli rushed to the nearby stream, collected some water in a coconut shell that she had and gave it to him. He swallowed the millet with the water.

She then offered him her food which he ate slowly, while his eyes were fixed on her.

'Valli, I thank you for the food and water. You have quenched my hunger and thirst. I have always been devoted to Muruga. Your father just said that you and your clan are slaves of Muruga and by extension slaves of his devotees. I am his devotee and I need someone to take care of me with love and affection. Marry me, for only two people can take care of someone with utmost love and care: one is a mother and the other is a spouse. I am too old to have you as my mother, become my wife,' said the old man.

Much like Parvati was confounded on her first encounter with Mahadeva, Valli was too. She just had an encounter with a hunter who asked her to marry her. Now, another old man was doing the same. What was with all these men today, she wondered. She was also incensed at the audacity of the old man, at his age, to ask for someone as young and vibrant as her to marry him.

'Sir, considering your age and your claimed devotion towards Muruga, I will reply in a kind manner. I will marry no one but Muruga himself. I just refused the proposal from a virile, young and handsome hunter. What makes you think that I would marry someone as old as yourself?

'You said only two people can take care of someone with utmost care. There is one more person; it is the daughter. Even though I am young enough to be your granddaughter, I will accept you as my father. I will leave my father Nambiraja, and come and take care of you, accompanying you wherever you go. But my heart, body and soul will always belong to Muruga. If there is a marriage in my life, it will be with Muruga and Muruga alone, as I believe it is willed by Muruga himself,' said Valli.

'I am indeed unfortunate. May Muruga bless you and grant you your wish,' blessed the old man as he got up to leave.

Valli quickly made a leaf packet, gathered some food and gave it to the old man for his journey, bidding him farewell.

No sooner did the old man take a few steps forward than she heard an elephant call out very close to her tower. Her eyes darted everywhere in fear and she noticed that the elephant was right in front of her, on the pathway to the tower. The old man, who was walking through the field, had avoided it.

The elephant was gigantic. It had long curved tusks with pointed ends. Its eyes were red and there was hole on the side of its forehead from which musth was oozing. Her worst fears were confirmed. The elephant was in a state of testosterone-driven madness and such elephants are the most dangerous creatures in any forest.

Her legs froze in fear. Her hands were clasped tight. She started to sweat profusely. Her father would have reached their kingdom now and would be out of earshot. The hunter too was nowhere to be seen. All she could see was the old man walking away from her. The elephant's eyes were completely focussed on her. It rushed at her and she jumped up, caught the creeper and climbed up the tower, trying to take her spear as she moved. Before she could even touch the spear, the elephant hit the tower and it went crashing to the ground with her. Without her spear, she knew she was no match for the beast.

She then recollected that the old man had said that he is used to roaming in forest. He probably knew how to handle such an elephant. The elephant, having torn down the tower, turned her attention to her. She landed close to the old man in one leap and rushed to him while the elephant was still aggressively staring at her.

As soon as she touched him, he turned to her and asked, 'What is it my child? Have you changed your mind?'

'Ele...ele...elephant!' she stammered.

'Where?' he asked, turning his attention behind her. He saw the elephant. He saw that she was terrified of it.

He told her, 'Accept my marriage proposal and I shall save you. If not, let us both perish at the feet of the elephant. I have spent enough time in the forest to know how to handle such elephants.

But if I were to live without you, I would rather die with you. Say that you accept me as your husband.'

The shiver in his voice was gone. He spoke clearly and without a hint of the stammer associated with his age. She also noticed that he was upright now and did not have the hunch anymore. Her eyes darted to the elephant and she realized that she had little choice. Die or accept the marriage proposal, for the old man was not joking.

'I... I accept. I accept you as my husband,' said she.

The old man asked her to move behind him. He stood up and took in a lung full of air, expanding his frame to make him look bigger than he really was. The elephant let out a loud cry.

He lifted the stick he used for walking over his head with both his hands. His left hand freed the stick as he spun it in the air with his right hand and then he threw it in front of the elephant.

The elephant saw the stick that was lying between the two as if a line had been drawn. It looked at the enlarged frame of the old man. It turned around and left. Once behind the trees, it transformed to Ganesha and then disappeared.

Valli, who had her eyes closed, opened her eyes slowly at the complete silence. She looked where the elephant had been standing. It was no longer there. She realized that she now was in the embrace of the old man, her husband. She also came to the realization that she now can no longer belong to Muruga. Having resigned herself to her fate and having given her word to the old man, she asked, 'Dear old man, I have given you my word and have accepted you as my husband, it is my duty as it is my fate to be your wife and serve you. Command me and I shall do as you order. Do you want me to take you to my father and narrate all that has happened so that he can arrange for you to be crowned the king of our tribe as per our custom?'

'No, Valli. All I sought was your love and care and that is all I seek. I am going to worship Muruga in the forest. I will come back to get you. When I come back, we can inform your father of what happened and I will take you with me as I leave for the next Muruga temple,' said the old man, who now had his hunch and the stammer in his voice.

'As you wish, my Swami,' said Valli.

The old man went to pick up his stick and went on his way towards the interior of the forest in search of a Muruga temple.

Valli went back to the tower and started to fix it. The thought of killing herself came but she brushed it aside, saying that she cannot do that to the old man whom she just married, but she also could not banish Muruga from her mind. Further, if she killed herself, she would never reunite with her lord. She calmed herself down with the belief that whatever was happening was happening according to her lord's will. Until Muruga wills, she decided to keep her word, both out of her honour as a princess as well as respect for tradition.

Kumba came to relieve her from her duty. She said nothing about the encounter with the elephant and went back to her kingdom. Nambiraja was happy to see her safe but could see that something was eating her. He chose not to prod her about it and simply let her be.

Marriage

Months passed and the harvest of millets was completed, with no sign of either the old man or Muruga. She left the burden to her god and decided to do her duty, hoping that the events with the old man and the elephant had been a nightmare and none of it had really happened.

The day came for clearing out the fields for the next sowing. Valli volunteered for the task.

She went to the farm that had been cleared and started to crush all the leftover fragments into the soil, allowing the soil to naturally use the crops' remains to nourish itself.

As she was almost done, she heard a voice calling, 'Valli!'

The voice had a stammer familiar to her. It was the old man. She did not even know his name. She turned around: it was indeed him and he looked older than before. He still had the bent back, his stick that he used to support his walk and his long beard. She went to him and bowed to him.

'I am hungry,' said he to her.

She opened the food she had packed for herself and gave it all to him. While he was eating, she went to collect to water for herself. When he finished, the old man said that he was tired and wanted to sleep. He looked around for a support for his head.

Valli said, 'Swami. Lie down on my lap.' He, after all, was her husband; the husband chosen for her by her lord, who had sent him in place of his divine self. She decided that from that moment onwards, she would be absolutely devoted to him, for he had come back for her and, unlike her god, had not deserted her. She gently pressed his forehead to allow him to sleep.

Meanwhile, in the kingdom, Narada came to meet Nambiraja and said, 'Congratulations! You did not tell me that you got your daughter married. I would have loved to come and bless her.'

'What do you mean, Rishi! I did not marry her off to anyone. She would not marry anyone but Lord Muruga himself,' said Nambiraja.

'Well, I just came through the forest and your millet farm. I saw that in the tower, she was seated after performing her duties only as a devout wife would to a husband, feeding him, giving him water and making him lie down in her lap,' Narada said.

Nambiraja became irate. He trusted Narada completely and believed that he would not lie. He summoned all his men and asked them to come with him to the millet farm to investigate the matter, for he believed that his daughter would never have willingly allowed anyone but Muruga to touch her, which meant that it must be a demon who had entranced her into allowing him to do so.

Just as he was about to leave, the men who had left with Veeramartanda returned and joined him in his quest to the millet farm. They all rushed out once they heard from Nambiraja about what had happened, out of concern, worry and anger. They all reached the place and as Narada had told them, the sight of their princess seated with a strange man sleeping on her lap made them go wild with rage. They all ran towards her, but were stopped by the raised hand of Valli.

'My husband is sleeping. I will not allow anyone to disturb him. Go away, otherwise you will incur my wrath!' warned Valli.

'But, my child! You were to marry none but Muruga. I am sure that this old man is the same one who came the other day and is a demon in disguise who has entranced you with some vile magic trick, making you believe that he is your husband and you are his wife. We shall slay the demon and set you free,' said Nambiraja as the rest agreed.

'No, Father. He is no demon. He saved my life from the attack of a mad elephant. In return, he asked me to marry him. I accepted, taking it as Lord Muruga's will. Young or old, demon or human, he is my husband and I am his wife. I will not accept any more slander towards him, Father. Speak one more ill word about him and I will disown myself as your daughter,' said Valli.

Nambiraja would have none of it. He ordered his men to attack the old man while Valli stood shielding him. The old man got up and stood straight. He said, 'Valli. Hide behind me. I will handle them as I did the mad elephant.'

She obeyed his words and went behind him. They all threw their spears at him. The old man spun his stick, creating a wind tunnel that threw all the spears back at them, striking them wherever they had aimed for on the old man's being. They all fell.

Nambiraja threw his sword at him. The old man hit the sword back with his stick, directing it back at the king. The sword whizzed past Nambiraja, taking off his crown with and effectively tonsuring him at the crown of his head.

Valli, on seeing Nambiraja in danger, kneeled down and held the old man's feet saying, 'Swami! Forgive my father. We will leave this place. I am no longer his daughter or their princess. I am only your wife and all my being belongs to you. Spare their lives.'

The old man said, 'As you wish, my dear.' He then sent his stick like a boomerang. It spun over the slain warriors as well as Nambiraja, restoring them to how they had been.

The stick rebounded and was caught by a man whose beauty was unparalleled. He was the hunter who had come that first day, but now he was clad in a royal manner, replete with the choicest of jewels. The stick became a Vel as soon as he touched it.

The warriors who had been with Veeramartanda quickly recognized him as Muruga and prostrated before him shouting, 'Vetri Vel! Veera Vel!' The rest of the clan understood who he was and they too did the same, as did Nambiraja.

Valli looked up, seeing her kith and kin alive and well, prostrating before her husband. She was in complete and utter shock. Her husband, the old man, was none other than the one who she had sought all her existence and had always wanted to marry. It was her lord and god. She wanted to speak but not a word came out of her mouth. She wanted to cry but not a tear escaped her eye. She was stunned.

'Get up, Valli!' said Muruga kindly. 'You place is not at my feet but by my side.'

She coyly got up and stood. The usually loquacious Valli was reticent. She was radiant. Tears flowed from Nambiraja's eyes, seeing the divine picture of his daughter, who now was goddess Valli.

Nambiraja said, 'My lord, as our son-in-law, we request you to come to our kingdom and accept our hospitality.'

Muruga said, 'Not only I, but my parents and my brothers, including the one whom Valli has already met, will come to your kingdom to solemnize our wedding and make it known to the world.'

As promised by Muruga, Mahadeva, Parvati and Ganesha, along with Avvai and Agastya, came to Thanigai, which now became Thiruthanigai. His ten siblings, including Jwala, took part in the celebrations. They had a grand reception and the union of Valli and Muruga was celebrated in the tribal kingdom, according to the customs of Valli's tribe. Valli was in bliss and the couple was blessed by Narada, Mahadeva and Parvati, Ganesha, of whom Valli was no longer afraid, and her own family and tribe.

They all left for their abodes while Muruga took Valli to Thiruparankundram, where he was residing with Devayani.

Harmony

*D*evayani was heartbroken when she heard the news that Muruga was arriving with his newlywed second wife, Valli. She was drowning in sorrow, waiting to confront her husband about his infidelity.

Muruga and Valli reached their home and were stopped at the entrance by Devayani. Devayani, who was usually softspoken and spoke one word in place of two, had the choicest of words for them, fuelled by her emotional state.

Just as she was about to open her mouth, Muruga called her, 'Devayani, meet your younger sister.'

'She is not my younger sister, my lord, and if you want me, she shall not be your wife either,' said Devayani.

'We both love Muruga, sister,' said Valli, taking a cue from Muruga, for his words always had greater meaning and truth. 'We both married him. I am as much his wife as you are, and you are as much his wife as I am.'

'I have nothing to say to you nor do I want to hear you speak. My issue is with my husband who betrayed me. I have no anger towards you nor any love for you,' said Devayani as she turned her attention to Muruga.

'I concede, my lord, that our marriage was arranged as a part of the great war. Even if I came as a prize, I was still dutiful and devoted to you, as expected of a wife. I did all my duties diligently and did everything that was in my capacity to keep you happy. If there was something amiss, you should have told me. It is not right, my lord, that you married another woman, especially keeping me in the dark about it until after the event.

'You never gave me a chance to correct myself and be the wife you sought. Had you given me the chance and had I failed in it, I would have been the first person to celebrate your second marriage,' said Devayani with tears in her eyes.

'Neither of you remember your past as I decreed. It is time I enlightened you about who you truly are,' said Muruga. 'Devayani, you are not Indra's daughter, and I did not marry you as a gift for winning the war. You are the daughter of my uncle, Mahavishnu. He directed you to do penance for me and seek me for your husband.

'Valli, you too are the daughter of Mahavishnu and the twin sister of Devayani. You too participated in penance with your sister. I appeared, pleased with both your devotion, and granted you the boon. I tasked both of you to reach Indra and Nambiraja. I set things in motion for you two to be adopted by them. Both of you know this to be true, for both of you were adopted as you have known for ages.

'Devayani performed her penance without breaking for food, water or rest and hence she led a comfortable life as Indra's daughter and reached me directly without going through any trouble. You, Valli, only worshipped me with utter devotion and regular prayer. Hence, you had to go through the trouble that you faced during the courtship, before you reached me.

'It is both your destiny to reach me and thus, I have granted you the boon you both sought in unison. May you both recollect the truth that I erased from your minds,' said Muruga.

At that instant, their minds cleared up and they saw their whole life as if it were a film being played in their heads. The illusions of being Indra's daughter and Nambiraja's daughter cleared up. Valli and Devayani ran and hugged each other once they realized that they were long lost sisters.

Devayani said, 'Forgive me, my lord, for the harsh words that sprang from my ignorance.'

'All is forgiven. Let us go home now. Thiruparankundram belongs to Devayani while Thiruthanigai belongs to Valli. Pazhamudhircholai is where we will be, for that was where I had the sweetest of encounters of my life with a beautiful old lady, Avvai,' said Muruga.

They all left for Pazhamudhircholai and lived there to bless his devotees.